Nobody Told Me

Karla Rogers

DEDICATIONS

This book is dedicated to my brother Kevon, who reminded me who I was before I was a mom, to give me inspiration for who I can be now.

I am also dedicating this book to my family, who sacrificed so much of our time together to allow me to chase my dream. They showed me endless patience during my late nights, emotional and physical absences, and constant questions and requests for "5 more minutes." This book is for you and because of you.

This book is also dedicated to the memory of two people who passed this year who taught me the value of unconditional love. They always believed in me, and I hope I made them proud.

Jack Leonard Anson 7/10/1980-6/6/2021

David Leonard Langager 10/21/1962-5/9/2021

INTRODUCTION

Nobody told me having a child would change me from an ordinary woman to an ordinary woman in charge of a baby with absolutely no idea what to do.

Nobody told me these small humans would teach me more about life, and about myself, than anyone else in the world.

Nobody told me that I would have a child who would stop and speak to every stranger on the street with a motorcycle, a policeman's badge, or look in any way like his grandpa.

Nobody told me that you can and will watch Barney's Halloween Special 365 days a year.

Nobody told me that your child will have a favorite spoon, let alone a least favorite spoon.

Nobody told me that pregnancy and child-rearing books were full of absolute bullshit.

Nobody told me that your child can both break your heart and fill it in a single day. Not a single soul. Not one of those smiling faces at my baby shower. Not one of those old ladies who stopped to feel my belly without my permission. Nobody.

Nobody told me that when they leave you it changes everything.

Chapter 1 – The Beginning

I never intended to have children. Not in the *I hate kids* way but in the *I'm not super maternal, I'm going to fuck it up* kind of way. In retrospect, I was right. I'm not super maternal; but that's okay, I still got the job done. And I did fuck it up; I fucked up a lot. Something they don't tell you, and this is a complete insider secret: It's okay to fuck up. Kids are resilient and forgiving. Not always, of course, it will be a cold day in hell before my daughter doesn't remind me of the time I accidentally locked her in the car.

I also never intended to get married. I figured I'd fuck that up too, but I had always seen myself as an introvert, a solitudinarian. I had the misconception that because I was content being alone, it meant that I was destined to stay that way as if it was the only way I would be happy. Nobody told me that you can't just decide what's going to make you happy; you're either happy or you're not. I could have been happy alone, but I wouldn't have the things I have now, and I wouldn't trade any of that for the world.

At my first baby shower, everyone filled out index cards with *parenting advice*. Most of them were ridiculous, like my Aunt Marie's *whiskey on the gums for teething*; or Scott's Great Grandma Viv's *don't hold them too much or you'll spoil them*. I can't even count how many said *date night* or *make time for yourself* or *sleep when the baby sleeps*. All great advice in theory, but nearly impossible to maintain. There was one though, it had no name on it and 22 years later I still can't match the handwriting. It said, *do what feels right, and fuck everyone else.* I framed that one and hung it on the nursery wall until Jason was old enough to be able to read and ask what it meant, then I moved it to my office wall. I had subtly over the years asked everyone who had been at the shower if they knew who wrote it, but nobody did. It was not only the best parenting advice I'd ever received but became my life motto over the years.

My pregnancy with Jason was borderline FBI torture. I managed to throw up everything I ate for 9 months, yet somehow still gain 50 pounds. I craved foods that were so ridiculous that it was no wonder I threw up so frequently, my body was angry at me. I often worried that a difficult pregnancy was going to mean a difficult child and I really started questioning my life choices

As difficult as the pregnancy was for Jason, the delivery was as smooth as butter. I try not to brag about that except for every chance I get, which could be the title of my future memoir: *How to Lose Friends and Chase Away New Ones in a Single Conversation.*

The 9-month trip to Vomit Town instilled my initial feeling of not wanting children - I mean, obviously not Jason, he did not come with a gift receipt - I was stuck with that one – but there was no round-trip ticket in my future.

Jason was the easiest baby. He never cried, he slept well, he ate well, he met all his milestones early – it felt like a trap. Was I missing something? What was coming next? When my friends complained about the lack of sleep or the crying or the tantrums, I just smiled and nodded and agreed, because to do otherwise was met with looks of disbelief and speculation. My favorite was the follow-up phrase of *just wait until the next one*.

The older Jason got the more we were prodded about a second child. It would have been easier, albeit a blatant lie, to claim that we had been unable to conceive again than to say we were terrified the second one would be difficult. In the end, we just said that Jason was all that we needed. It turns out that sometimes the most unexpected surprises are exactly what you need. Nobody told me that although the second child very well could be difficult, it can also mean rewarding, challenging, and the ray of sunshine you didn't know you were missing.

My pregnancy for Avery was nearly willed into place by Jason. He wanted a sister so badly that he just decided to tell people he was having one. I had to explain to everyone that he was just saying he wanted one, not that we were having one. However, when the pregnancy test shows a surprise positive result within a few weeks, you have to start worrying about wizardry heritage in your 5-year-old and checking the mailbox for letters from Hogwarts. As expected, the pregnancy was a cake walk in comparison. I craved the simple food of *Gummy Life Savers* rather than gritty chocolate milk, mayonnaise, and green olive juice. I threw up zero times. I looked like a glowing Christmas angel. Okay, that went too far. I felt good. Avery's birth was so smooth and quick I barely had time to take my shoes off at the hospital.

Avery rounded out our household like I never expected. Was she difficult? Let's call it challenging. She baffled Jason. She was a tropical storm, and he was a cloudless summer day. She was loud to his quiet. She was extreme to his mellow.

She was angered quickly, she cried frequently. She flipped through extreme emotions like a flickering light bulb in a haunted house. She was a daddy's girl from the minute her hand wrapped around his pinky. Being a daddy's girl did not keep her from also being a mama's girl or even a brother's girl – it meant she had the whole house enraptured.

Six years apart is a large age gap for two kids. They were always at completely different stages of their lives; however, in Jason's senior year I realized something - six years was the perfect gap. I didn't plan it this way, but I like to pretend I did. At the time Jason would graduate high school and leave for college, Avery be just starting 8th grade. By the time Jason graduated from college, Avery would just be starting her senior year and preparing to graduate herself and leave for college. Essentially, my kids would leave home in a slow, drawn-out manner, easing my pain somewhat. Or so I thought.

Nobody told me that I would be very wrong about all of that.

Chapter 2 – The Trouble with Avery

What I considered the end of my predictable, typical days came on a Friday in October. It was unseasonably warm, and I was watering the plants on the deck and drinking my coffee. The phone rang and the caller ID showed South Medler High School. Avery was a junior there. I groaned and put the phone back in my pocket. Most often these calls were reports of Avery causing a disruption in class. She frequently challenged teachers and authority figures. She was the smartest person in that school by a landslide and they were terrified of her. I decided to let it go to voicemail. She was never actually in trouble, they just wanted Scott and I to try to get her to stop speaking her mind and we absolutely would not. She was a strong, independent, intelligent young woman, and she had every right to stand up and speak when she disagreed with something, especially when it came to the quality and content of her education.

Once back inside I sat at my desk and brought up my email account. I had a house to show that day and a few more listings I was hoping to schedule showings for, maybe later that afternoon or the next day. There was also a new client that I was dying to take on. Their home was beautiful and would likely sell fast and bring in a tidy commission. I hoped that it would mean a real Christmas vacation in December. After Jason graduated from college in June, who knew what the future would hold? I shook my head to clear that unwelcome thought.

The first email that popped up was from Reid Jenkins, Avery's guidance counselor. It was just then that I remembered the voicemail.

Dear Mr. and Mrs. Fowler,

I'd like to schedule a meeting with both of you in my office today at 1:00 if possible. Please let me know if that will work for you. Avery is not in trouble, I promise.

Reid Jenkins.

Within seconds a reply came from Scott's email account at work.

Molly and I will be there.

Scott Fowler

I looked at my calendar. My showing was at 12:30, there was no way I could make it. I dialed Scott's cell number. I was a little annoyed that he hadn't even checked with me before agreeing to the meeting.

"I can't be there at 1:00, Scott, I have a showing at 12:30." I blurted out as soon as he answered.

"Reschedule it, Molly, this is more important," He said quickly, obviously in a hurry. I closed my eyes and took a deep breath. He always thought everything was more important than my job.

"You know what this is about and what they're going to say, it's really not going to be that important. She probably corrected the spelling and grammar in Mrs.

Darby's email and hit *reply all*. Remember when she did that?" I snorted. I've never seen a woman's face so red. She was furious. So much for an English teacher. "I'm going to ask Reid to reschedule." I pulled the email back up and began to type. I didn't feel the need to reschedule my day again just for that.

"Don't reschedule. I'll be at the school at 1:00 whether you're there or not. He said she wasn't in trouble, and whatever it is, it's about Avery, and that's important to me." He hung up. I stared at the computer screen for a long time until the screen saver started. It was a slideshow of pictures I'd taken of the kids over the years. I quickly closed the laptop. I knew I was being a little selfish by wanting to reschedule, and looking at their sweet faces would make me feel guilty. However, I was a little curious about what he called this meeting for. They hardly ever called us both in together, and if he said she wasn't in trouble and it was important, then maybe Scott was right and we should go. The problem was that I also felt a little anxious about what he might say. I couldn't put my finger on why, but something about this meeting was making me nervous.

I took a sip of my coffee and winced when I found it had gone cold. I opened the laptop again and stared at the email I had begun earlier for a few minutes contemplating my options. I clicked the X in the corner. I began the process of rescheduling today's showing. I had to work with both the client and the homeowner to coordinate dates and times that worked for everyone. The entire process took about 45 minutes of back and forth and in the end I could tell neither party was happy about it. Neither was I.

***

I arrived at the school 15 minutes early. I saw a figure leaning against the wall outside the office and I couldn't help but smile. Avery was slouched against the wall in a tight pencil skirt and button-down shirt, as if she were waiting for a job interview. When she wasn't rocking her overtly studious look, she dressed like she was on her way to a 1920s ballet, complete with funky accessories. Today's was a golden pocket watch pendant she found at the neighbor's yard sale. She didn't look up from her French copy of Les Mis as I approached

"Dad's on his way," I said as I got closer. She looked up from her book and smiled at me. "Do you know what this is about?" I asked.

She shook her head. She actually looked a little nervous, something I don't see very often. "I haven't done anything or said anything at all recently, I swear."

Scott rounded the corner. His dark hair and green eyes were what made the women still double-take at 47 years old, but his incredible sense of humor and his dedication to his kids were the things that made my heart soar. Along with the other things, of course. I was no longer annoyed with him. He put his kids first and it was the right thing to do. I could and should learn more from him. He didn't look surprised to see me; he knew I'd be there. He hugged Avery tight. His girl. He would give her the whole universe if she asked.

"What did the school do to you now, Aves? Do I have to fight someone?" He put his dukes up dramatically, ready to defend his girl from every threat in the world. This made her laugh as usual.

He winked at me over her head. At that moment Reid Jenkins, a short balding man with thick glasses, nervously poked his head out the door to let us know he was ready for us.

The office was way too small for four people, and I could feel the oxygen drain from it and sweat start to form at the nape of my neck. Stress or heat, I couldn't tell, maybe both. I held out hope that Reid would make this an in-and-out meeting. I hated when they tried to shame us for supporting our child. Even worse, when they tried to shame Avery. It didn't sit right with me. She made waves, she shook foundations, and I wouldn't let them stop her.

This very office was filled with days like this one, conversations about what we should be doing about Avery and her disruptions. I refused to tell my child that when she finds information being taught incorrectly to stay silent just because it was embarrassing to the staff. I suggested more than once that maybe they should improve the quality of their staff and educational tools first. I prepared myself for another fight, another showdown. Nobody told me I was preparing for the wrong battle.

Reid slid a piece of paper across the table toward us. "It was brought to my attention this morning that Avery is eligible for graduation this year." The piece of paper was a consent form for early graduation. He pulled a pen from his drawer and held it out to me. I stared at the black pen suspended in midair, unable to move my arms. After realizing I wasn't going to grab it immediately, he gently set it down in front of me on the desk. I turned to look at Scott and then Avery. She was beaming. "Did you know about this?" I asked her. She shook her head. Scott was speechless, his face white.

"Avery, did you take some online courses over the summer?" Reid asked as he handed her another piece of paper. They were her transcripts marked up with a yellow highlighter.

"Yea, I do every summer. I like to learn." She shrugged. "Is that a bad thing?"

"Only that they cost a fortune." Scott laughed. "But there are worse things I could spend my money on than my daughter's education." He patted Avery's back and then cracked his knuckles. He did that when he was nervous.

"Well, Mr. Fowler, it was a smart investment. A lot of the students here take the PE and health courses to open up space for electives. Not many students are like Avery, who continued on to take more classes. Some of those courses actually do count towards high school credits. Some don't, of course, but Avery now has enough credits to graduate in June, one year ahead of the rest of her class. You just need to sign the form." His smile was almost as big as Avery's. I'm not sure if he was genuinely happy for her or excited to see her go.

Scott and I looked at each other for a long time, neither of us wanting to pick up the pen but knowing we had to. A million thoughts and words bounced around in my head. It felt fast. I wanted to run away. I waited for him to shake his head no, give me permission to break her heart. The tears in his eyes matched the pit in my stomach. I felt a tap on my shoulder. I looked at Avery, her face a mixture of hope, fear, and excitement. She handed me the pen. I looked back at Scott, who gave me a quick nod and then looked away discreetly, wiping his eyes, not wanting his girl to see him as anything but strong and proud. I signed the paper before my own tears fell. I didn't hide them.

I excused myself to the restroom. I walked briskly down the hall, to the farthest one I could find. Far away. I wasn't sure why I was crying. This was incredible. My daughter was going to graduate at 16. What an accomplishment. My baby. I was looking forward to this. Next year. Not today. I watched in the mirror as the tears continued to fall. I wiped each one away as they fell, begging them to stop. Be strong, be more like Scott.

You're proud of her, Molly, knock it off. What's wrong with you?

I walked back toward the counseling office. I moved slower, hoping to slow time down. I wondered momentarily if I just walked out the door, got in my car and went home, maybe I could erase the day. I could go back to bed and find this was just a bad dream. As I walked toward the office, I glanced briefly at the glass door leading to the parking lot, considering the temptation. I grabbed the counseling office door and opened it. I crossed my fingers that we were done and they were ready to leave, but they were still seated in the stuffy office, going through brochures and more paperwork. They were talking about college applications, scholarships, deadlines, college acceptance rates, Ivy League application fees. The pit in my stomach was getting heavier with each word. I had no one to blame but myself. I had signed the paper. It was my signature on it. Me. I could have put my foot down. I could have said *absolutely not*. I could have been the bad mother. Yes, she would have hated me. She would have cried, screamed, cursed. But she would have done it here. At home. With me. *Do what feels right and fuck everyone else.* Holding my daughter back did not feel right, but neither did any of this.

I needed to go home and pretend it wasn't happening for a few hours. The phone calls will happen. The news will spread. Later. I wanted to take these last few hours of what I had left of normalcy and cherish them. I felt guilty for feeling that way, but I felt like I was being robbed. Part of her childhood was being taken from me. The time I thought I had left, gone. The swish of the pen sealed my fate, putting an expiration date on her childhood. My job as a mother, one I cherished, would become less and less relevant until it is no longer needed at all. I always knew this day would come. The empty nest they call it. You prepare for it, at least that's what they say. Nobody told me there was no way to truly prepare for it, because it's nothing like you expect it to be, and that it comes out of nowhere, and it runs right over your heart.

CHAPTER 3 – THE TWIN THING

It was decided that we would celebrate Avery's news at The Salty Dog that evening with Jason and his girlfriend Hannah. They had been together for six years and she had become a part of the family. The Salty Dog was one of nine bars owned by my brother Miles. He was happy to have us and host the celebration dinner for his niece.

It was supposed to be just a quiet evening with our family and Miles, but when Scott and I walked through the door, I saw a banner hanging up that said, *Congratulations Avery*. He had white and gold helium balloons covering the ceiling and tied to every table and chair. Her favorite colors. He had a cake on the table, one that came from Sweet Dreams, the bakery downtown that Avery loved. The owner, Laura, was a talented cake artist. The cake had white frosting and was more than likely chocolate cake since it was her favorite. The top had a shockingly realistic cartoon of Avery on top of the world, wearing a cap and gown and holding Thor's hammer. In purple writing, it said *Avery Conquers the World*. It was incredibly well done and probably took her hours to do. Her normal turn-around time is a minimum of seven days. Laura clearly put a rush on it; I can't imagine how much Miles paid for a same-day order. He had huge platters with all of Avery's favorite foods covering three tables along the wall. Four different warming trays of buffalo wings, all with various sauces ranging from medium to mango habanero. He wisely put a warning next to the hottest one. There were platters of vegetables and hummus. On the last table, there were warming trays with different kinds of pasta. This was enough food to feed everyone in town for two weeks. It was all a bit excessive, but that was Miles. He didn't do anything halfway, especially for his family.

The room was packed with people from all over town. Once Miles learned of Avery's news, he spread the word and people showed up for her. We lived in a very small area, and everyone either knew one of the Fowlers or Miles, or knew of us, and they all came out to congratulate a girl who was surely going to change the world. I looked over and saw her swarmed by people she knew, people she didn't know, friends, acquaintances, family. Avery didn't have a lot of close friends, but there were a lot of kids from her school present. They all respected her, and they came armed with cards and gift bags. She had the biggest smile on her face being the current center of attention. She was glowing.

Scott and I stood in the doorway, stunned at the extravagant display. I felt my body tense up at the excitement and overall joyous atmosphere, felt the pit in my stomach fill with dark angry feelings. I was not ready for this. The emotions I felt did not match the overall atmosphere. I looked around the room and saw all the smiling faces, all these people who already heard the news, and I immediately wanted to turn around and run away. What the hell were they so happy about? Happy that my daughter was breaking my heart?

I turned to Scott, hoping to be able to share my feelings with another person, my partner, but he was beaming as he scanned the room, reveling in the celebration over the impending loss of our children. I reeled at the thought that I was the only one who felt that way. Was I being selfish or was he being naive? Was I justified in my anger or was he being heartless? I needed to leave. I couldn't do this. Scott caught my hand just before I made what would have been a truly selfish decision. I looked at him, saw the confusion and wonder in his eyes. *Ask me, Scott. Ask me how I feel about this.* Nothing.

I heard my name boom from the sound system. Miles was standing on the stage with a microphone in hand. My brother. My tension eased and I took a deep breath. I forced a smile for Scott. I'm just going to have to fake it, I guess. Suddenly, *Good Golly Miss Molly* began playing from the speakers. I rolled my eyes and laughed.

The music quieted down and while he and nearly everyone in the building had their eyes on me he said, "You all know my sister, Molly, right? Of course you do, you wouldn't be here if you didn't. Oh wait, I forgot about the free food!" Laughter rang through the crowd. All eyes seemed to be locked on me. "The other day my sister bet me $100 that I couldn't build a working car out of spaghetti." The crowd seemed to finally return their attention back to the wisecracker on the stage, probably expecting a fascinating story about building a vehicle. He whipped out a $100 bill and said, "You should have seen the look on her face when I drove pasta." The crowd roared as he theatrically pretended to drive a wobbly car. I closed my eyes and shook my head, cringing at his awful jokes.

I watched him delight in the attention, bantering with Kevin, one of his friends from school; winking at someone in the audience, likely a girl hoping to get some individual attention later. My heart filled with pride. He was a natural leader and commanded everyone's attention without asking for it, although he usually did anyway. He was the life of every party; hell, he was the host of all the parties.

He picked up his guitar and pointed at Avery, "I wanna sing a song with my niece, you know which one." *Oh no.* I closed my eyes and moaned. I heard her squeal and clamor onto the stage and grab another microphone. He began the opening chords of *No Children* by *The Mountain Goats*. They both loved that band, and that song was their favorite. The lyrics were ridiculous, but the place went crazy. They got to the last verse and Avery was already unable to control the giggles; this was her favorite part of the song. Miles knew that, so he looked at her and they belted it out together. I cringed.

After their duet, Miles came over and hugged me. "You went a little overboard on the party, Uncle Miles." I punched him playfully in the gut. "And you just had to sing that song, didn't you?"

"I knew it would bug you and I love to watch you squirm." He paused for a second and in a quiet voice added "Are you doing okay?"

I broke down. The tears I begged to stop in the school bathroom began to flow again. *Okay?* It was the first time that day anyone had asked me if I was okay. It was also the first time I acknowledged that I was not okay. I wanted to be, I should be, I thought I had to be, but I was not at all okay. He led me to his office and handed me some tissues and a mirror.

"Do I look that bad?" I asked as I took the mirror from him.

"Way worse than usual," He said with a laugh. I slapped his shoulder and wiped the mascara off my face.

I sat down in his big leather chair and sighed. "How'd you know? Nobody else seems to notice."

He grabbed a chair across the room and brought it closer to me and sat down. He looked at me solemnly and said, "It's the twin thing, I could feel your sadness."

I groaned. "We aren't twins, dumbass; stop telling people that. But if you looked like me maybe you'd actually have a girlfriend," I joked.

"Oh, really? How many girlfriends do you have?" He said as he pulled a bottle of tequila from a cabinet and poured two shots. It was his most expensive bottle, of course; nothing but the best for family. "Also, people do notice, I'm the only one who asked because you're an ugly crier and I think it's funny." He tapped his glass with mine. "To my niece Avery, the smartest girl I've ever known, with great taste in music," He said.

"To the best brother in the world, who keeps me grounded and humble," I said. He looked away. He was a softie and extremely conceited, but he also had a hard time accepting compliments.

We talked a bit about Avery and her possible plans. He asked what colleges she was looking at. I shrugged and ran my finger around the rim of the shot glass absentmindedly. He knew as well as I did where she wanted to go. She had been talking about it since she was nine. He didn't say the word and neither did I. Columbia. New York City. 2,857 miles away. 42 hours by car without stopping, which is exactly what I would do. He caught on rather quickly that I wasn't wanting to discuss this, so he gratefully changed the subject to something easier.

"Jason's also graduating this year, right? We're going to have a hell of a party here at the Dog in June!" He chuckled, but I didn't. Too soon. "Has Jason thought about what he's doing with his fancy degree after graduation?" That's better, I thought. I can talk about that.

"No, it's too early to get job offers, it's only October, but he'll probably end up at some company in Seattle," I said with a sigh, thankful I had one child I could count on to not tear my world apart. "He and Hannah will probably get married sometime next year. They've been saving money for their future and I've been keeping my eye out for good listings for rent or sale here in the area and also North Valley. Hannah will probably teach there; she's mentioned that she wanted to more than once."

Miles leaned his head back and pretended to snore. "Have you noticed that you have said the word *probably* a lot and that these are not only *your* plans but *your* life?" He poked me in the arm. "Have you actually asked *HIM* what he wants to do?" I squirmed and felt the sudden urge to defend myself. But he was right. Jason was my predictable child. He and Hannah had been together for years. They went to the same college. They had both decided to commute to school and work to earn money for their future. It was responsible. It was predictable. It was Jason. But we never really talked about the future, it was just expected. My silence must have said everything because he poured two more shots and we clinked glasses without words or cheer. As soon as the second tequila went down the office door opened.

Scott poked his head in. "Thanks for the invite." He grabbed the bottle and poured himself a shot. Miles stood and slapped Scott on the back. "Sorry, it was a twin thing. Congrats, man, you and my ugly sister did a great job. Also, it's a good thing Avery takes after her uncle because she's smart *AND* good looking!" He opened the office door again and turned back toward us. "Now get out of my office, I want to talk to my nephew."

I heard my brother's voice boom over the crowd noise as he stepped into the main room. "Hey, Jason! Get over here, I want to show you something in my office!" As Scott and I were leaving I shot Miles a look of warning. *Don't butt in.* He just shrugged and said "What? I just want to talk to my nephew? Go get a drink at the bar, Mols, relax." He pulled the door shut behind them, ready to pull an Uncle Miles hat trick.

As Scott and I walked back to the party he kissed my hand and smiled. The smile didn't quite reach his eyes. Maybe I wasn't the only sad one. Maybe I wasn't going to be alone. Nobody told me that the worst kind of alone is the one that comes after you've pushed everyone else away.

CHAPTER 4 – THE GUT GAMES

To my surprise I didn't dread the holidays as much as I thought I would. The upheaval of my life that was coming in the next year was placed firmly in the basement of my mind. The lights were turned off. The door was shut. It wasn't even on my mind at all. Except it was.

Avery's news did fade out. After a while, it didn't become the topic of every conversation, and on the outside, it looked as if nothing had changed. Everyone went back to work, back to school, back to regular everyday life. She wouldn't really start the college application process until after Thanksgiving, and she already knew where she was applying, so it wasn't really a regular dinner table topic anymore.

I threw myself into work. Taking the family away for a special Christmas became my main focus. It was a distraction from all of this, but I also wanted to give my family the best Christmas ever. I wanted to sell a house that would bring in a decent enough commission to allow for that. I had been looking at this resort in Cabo. All-inclusive. I couldn't wait to tell them. In order to make this happen, I would need to have a home sold by Thanksgiving, but even then I would have to take an advance on the commission. That was a dangerous game to play and just thinking about it made me nervous.

Thanksgiving week came around and I still hadn't been able to close a deal that would allow me to book the Cabo trip. I wondered briefly if was because my heart wasn't in it anymore. Maybe pieces of my heart were dying slowly and this was the first to fall. I knew the housing market was slow. We talked about it all the time in our meetings. The economy was hitting a slow patch. Many of our agents had started taking second or even third jobs. Buyers were becoming less and less. I mourned the probable loss of Cabo Christmas.

I stopped by the Dog one day for lunch after a showing. Halfway through my burger Miles whipped me in the arm with a towel.

"Ow!" I grabbed my arm dramatically. "What the hell is wrong with you?"

"Spit it out, Molly, your miserable face is driving my customers away," He said. I told him about Cabo Christmas and the likelihood that it wouldn't happen now. He brought out his laptop and went to the website to check out the resort. "I'll go get my credit card, you're going to Cabo." On his way back from his office with his credit card in hand he said, "And when I say you, I mean all of us, including me. You can't go to Cabo without your favorite brother." He sat back down again. All of a sudden this felt wrong.

I grabbed the card out of his hand and said, "No."

"Come on, I have to be your favorite brother, you don't have any other ones." He reached for the card again, but I put it out of reach.

"I mean no, we aren't going. None of us are." The words came out and I didn't even realize what I was saying, but my gut knew, my heart knew. This wasn't really what I wanted. Cabo didn't feel right anymore, and somehow I knew I was doing the right thing. It felt right. I would have regretted not having a traditional

Fowler Christmas; the stockings, the ornaments that the kids made, the Christmas movies, the stories, the memories. These things would never go away, I felt that in my heart. They may change, and that's okay, but all the memories and the special ornaments would always be a part of our holiday. None of these things were going away, they would continue that year, and they would continue for years. Nobody told me that next Christmas would be the best one yet.

After revealing my unexpected enlightenment to my brother, yes my favorite one, he smiled and said, "That's what I was hoping you'd say. You figured it out on your own. Now give back my card." He grabbed his card from me and opened the laptop back up. "I'm still going."

***

Thanksgiving was always my favorite holiday, I couldn't believe there was a day just for eating. At least that's what it seems like when you're a little kid. Miles and I had an eating competition every year. We would pick a different food by random draw and see who could eat the most of it. He almost always won, except for the year it was the green bean casserole. I'm not sure he could even finish the first serving.

Miles and I stopped the games when cholesterol and love handles became more of a concern. He wanted to pass the tradition on to his niece and nephew, but the age difference was too big. Miles and I were less than two years apart so a 10-year-old boy and a 12-year-old girl could be a suitable match; however, a

7-year-old girl didn't stand a chance against a 13-year-old boy's appetite. That was the year I let Miles talk me into it. He made a big deal about it at the event and everyone was so excited about it. The food chosen was mashed potatoes. Avery is far too competitive to let her brother win anything, so she kept up with him. She technically won, but I was the true loser. It took me an hour to clean up the Mashed Potato Rocket that came out of her a few minutes later. I found a small dried clump of potato projectile in my hair the next day. I cursed my brother.

Our family Thanksgiving is celebrated on Friday, and it's very low-key with leftovers, games, and lots of laughter. On Thursday we do *The Salty Gobbler*. This started about 15 years ago. The story behind this is one of the reasons I love my brother so much. The year after he opened the first Salty Dog, he had several patrons ask if he was going to be open on Thanksgiving, which he wasn't. He discovered that many of his customers had no place to go for the holiday. He wanted to give these people a place to go, but he also didn't want to ask his staff to work. His original plan was to do all the work himself, cook, and also serve the dinner, but I wouldn't let that happen.

It started with Miles, Scott, and I alone with all of the preparation and cooking. Avery was too young to help, but Jason was 7 and helped with a lot of the prep and setting tables. We opened to the public and only closed the doors when we ran out of food. We didn't charge, but we accepted donations for the following year's feast.

Over the years the crowd got bigger, more volunteers showed up to help, and locals would stop by with food to donate as well. Every year the financial contributions became so abundant that Miles started donating the surplus to charity, and the number on that check grew every year.

**

On that particular Thanksgiving morning, I woke up with an energy I hadn't felt in quite some time. At the Dog, music played through the speakers all day. Everyone had a job, everyone did their part. I loved watching the people of the town, especially my family, step up and help make this day special. Avery and Jason were setting up the tables, they were laughing about something; they had a lifetime of inside jokes. Hannah was in the corner, filling centerpieces. I could tell she was singing along to the music.

Scott and Miles were outside overseeing the smokers. He had ten smokers in total, many of which were brought in by town residents to donate for use at this event. The smoked turkey was so popular last year that we decided to make it the only turkey served this year.

I watched two of my favorite people outside talking, laughing, bonding. I loved that Scott had accepted from the beginning that this giant man child with no immediate family of his own was going to be a big part of our lives forever.

I did a quick inventory of the food that had been provided, brought in, made here, and was still being made. Everything was on track. My eyes drifted to the table in the corner. Two long tables were filled with pies, and that was just the beginning. By the time the Gobbler started, the pie count would at least double from volunteers bringing in their contributions. It gave me an idea.

I stepped outside, interrupting the Boys Club. Scott pulled me into him and kissed my head. My heart was so full today. Everything was perfect.

"Hey, Miles, I have a question," I said.

He sat down on a lawn chair after pulling two beers from the cooler, tossing one to Scott. "No, Molly, we're not identical twins. You didn't get blessed with this." He vaguely gestured at his face. "I wish someone had told you sooner."

I rolled my eyes. "I'm serious, Miles." I walked closer to him, crouched down next to him and looked him in the eyes. "Do you think you can eat more pumpkin pie than me?"

***

After a two-decade hiatus, The Gut Games were back.

I knew as I was finishing the first full pumpkin pie that 46-year-old Molly was not capable of eating this much food. I could barely swallow that last bite. My stomach was dangerously close to rejecting everything, a Pumpkin Pie Rocket was preparing to launch. I had never hated pumpkin pie as much as I did at that moment.

My brother was a much larger person; a person who could and had finished an entire pizza, probably this week. I watched my family cheer me on. I heard the sound of metal hitting wood. I looked over and saw Miles reach over and attempt to grab another fork out of the utensil bin. At that moment Jason grabbed the whole bin and ran across the room, hoping to give his mother a fighting chance. The room broke out in laughter and cheers.

"Keeping going, Mom!!" Avery and Hannah clapped and cheered me on.

My brother yelled across the room to Jason. "Little do you know, I don't need a fork!" He grabbed the pie with his hands and shoved it into his face. Even if I wanted to eat more I couldn't, because I couldn't stop laughing. He looked like he did when he was 8, he did nearly the same thing, but back then he did it for attention, not necessity. Oh, who was I kidding, he was still doing it for attention.

I watched my brother's eyes dancing with laughter, his face covered in orange goo and pie crust. I tried to swallow the last piece of crust from the first pie. He was halfway through his second whole pie. He didn't look even remotely sick. I watched the crowd; at least half the town had moved through at some point that day, especially when they heard of the resurrected challenge. The owner of the sporting goods store brought a trophy for the winner.

None of this was about winning for me. I knew from the beginning that Miles would win, not just because there was no possible way I could beat him, but because even if I could, even if I somehow came close, I'd let him win. It was about the feeling of togetherness, happiness, a room full of people who had a common purpose, a common reason for being; a room full of people with genuine smiles on their faces. I needed to feel this.

I gave up. I threw in the towel. Miles started his victory dance. Other than the struggle to ignore the potential liftoff rumble in my stomach, I was happy, content. I loved all of this. I loved watching my brother do the running man, pieces of pie falling off his face onto the ground. He did the moonwalk past me, sticking his tongue out as he did, probably the most PG gesture he could think of. People were howling in laughter. This was the feeling I was looking for. My entire life has been spent making other people happy, starting with my little brother, then Scott, our children, my clients. Their smiles, their joy fulfilled me, made me smile. It was my motivation.

Nobody told me that when the kingdom goes home and the lights go out, the court jester no longer has a reason to smile.

CHAPTER 5 - THE MAMA BIRD

Christmas was not bad at all. I wouldn't let it be. One of our favorite traditions was watching Christmas movies. We watched as many as we could and nobody ever got upset when Scott recited all of Clark Griswold's lines verbatim. We all laughed at Buddy the Elf as if it were the first time we watched it.

Decorating the tree has always been a fun experience for us. Everyone has their favorite ornaments. A gold golf ball and a ceramic Santa with a long beard are Scott's ornaments. He insists they be hung up first. Avery has several, but a ballerina that lights up is her all-time favorite. There's a stocking that Jason made in art class in elementary school. It looked like it was made of gingerbread, but as he found out the hard way, it was not. The 'gingerbread' stocking with a bite taken out is Jason's favorite. All of them are my favorite. Every ornament has a reason and is attached to a part of the Fowler History forever. I had for a time felt fear about what our future Christmases would look like, but as I looked around at my family I somehow felt that fear dissipate. These four people, the Fowlers, would always find their way to each other. And they did. Nobody told me that if I just bottled up that Christmas revelation and ignored my destructive inner voice for the next nine months, I would have saved myself and my family from so much pain.

***

We had a lot of traditions in our house over the years, but New Year's Eve wasn't one of them. It was probably very much due to the fact that other than Avery in the later years, the Fowlers were not night owls. Miles always went away after Christmas to celebrate the New Year at a friend's cabin in Canada. He always left Pepper at our house, which was the highlight of Avery's Holiday season, as they were best buddies.

Miles had announced early in December that he wasn't going to Canada that year, he wanted to have an epic Salty Dog party. On the day after Christmas Miles, Scott, and I were sitting at the bar discussing party plans.

"Should I call it Salty Midnight?" He asked. "Maybe The Salty Kiss?"

I smiled. That actually was clever. "Yea, that sounds good." My heart wasn't in it, I was distracted, mentally restless. I couldn't focus on one thing. I thought about how many of these New Year's parties we could have had. How many were wasted? Our family would have enjoyed them, maybe watched movies or played games until midnight, and then toasted the New Year and spoke of resolutions and favorite memories from the previous year. Why did I think I needed to sleep; I could sleep any time I wanted. Guilt. Christmas was amazing, and I came out of it with a renewed feeling of positivity and peace, but I felt like I left it all in Santa's sleigh.

"Why don't you just call it The Salty New Year?" Scott added.

Miles pointed at him, and said: "That's the winner." He looked over at me and said "I'm disappointed that you didn't think of that, Molly. I thought you were smarter than that."

I didn't respond. I know he was goading me into a reply, but I felt like I didn't have anything of use to add to their conversation. I normally would have thrown some sarcastic retorts at him, but I just couldn't today; I didn't have the energy. I didn't even look up from the doodle I was working on. The yellow steno pad was supposed to have notes about the party, not poorly drawn trees and mountains. I didn't want to go to this party. It probably would just remind my kids that their mother preferred to get beauty sleep over spending time with them on the last day of the year. Every year. Selfish. I had never hated the holiday, but now I did. I despised it. New Year's Eve rolled into New Year's Day, January 1st. A brand new year. What came after that? Changes. Mayhem. This coming year would bring me nothing but pain. I would lose so much. Who would I be at the end of the year? What role would I have in my kids' life? My husband's? Mine? Who would I be? My panic button was pressed.

"Maybe I could call and see if *The Beatles* are free to perform." Miles joked. "I'll have Will Ferrell and John C. Reilly get on stage and perform *Stepbrothers* quotes all night, Molly loves that movie." He paused, waiting for a response. He thought he was hitting a nerve referencing a movie that he knew I despised. I didn't have the usual passion to argue about it right now. He continued. "Of course, *Clifford the Big Red Dog* will be here hanging out with Pepper. They'll perform a dance routine."

"Sounds good," I said, completely uninterested. Scott reached over and touched my sleeve. "Molly, are you okay?"

I threw my head up and smiled, not wanting anyone to see my selfish ugly side. "Yea, of course, sorry; I'm just tired." I grabbed my pen and said, "Where are we at now? Do you have a big enough shovel for Clifford's shit, or should I order one on Amazon?" Just then Pepper joined the conversation from her bed in the corner by letting out a *woof*.

"Clifford isn't coming, I was joking," Miles yelled over his shoulder. Pepper laid her head back down on her bed, with startling human-like disappointment on her face. I raised my eyebrow at Miles. "Yea, I speak dog. What? Like it's hard?" He said.

They resumed the party planning while I excused myself to the restroom. I examined myself in the mirror while I washed my hands. I wasn't sure why I was happy and hopeful one day and a miserable negative toad the next. None of the circumstances changed day-to-day. The next year of my life was going to be one of many changes. I had no idea what my life would be like this time next year. The loss of control and predictability was eating at me, but what was even worse was knowing that everything I do, everything I've done my entire life, for my family, my kids, was going to become unnecessary. I would be phased out.

I thought about the literal nest and the mama bird. The baby birds get bigger and stronger because the mother bird goes out and gets the worm and feeds them. When they're strong enough, they fly away. That's the end of the story. Nobody told me what happened to the mama bird or the nest. Because nobody cares.

On my way back from the bathroom I heard Miles say "Hey Molly, since you're up, Pepper's doing the potty dance, can you take her outside?" I glanced over to see the dog sleeping on her bed and looked back at him with confusion. "She doesn't do it in front of people, she's shy.." I looked at Scott, who as far as I knew was still considered *people*, then back at Miles. He said, "Okay, she just doesn't do it in front of you because you're mean and would laugh at her." I looked again at Scott, wondering if he's hearing this weird conversation or if I had come out of the bathroom into a different dimension.

Scott just shrugged his shoulders and said "I saw it."

I called for Pepper and headed for the back door. Before I shut the door behind me I said, "If she learned her dance moves from you, Miles, then I definitely would laugh at her."

Just before the door closed I heard Miles say to Scott, "See, I told you she's mean."

I leaned against the back door, waiting for Pepper to do her business. She sat down and stared at me. *What?* I thought. *Go! It's cold out here!* She whimpered a little but kept her eyes on me. I was about to go in and yell at Miles, tell him he was a liar, tell him he was the mean one. Instead, I got down and pulled Pepper in for a hug, buried my face in her fur. She let out a sweet doggy sigh and all the thoughts I had of the mama bird, the nest, Miles, the New Year's party, the miserable attitude I couldn't shake, and the fears of the coming new year and the changes to come disappeared.

Nobody told me that sometimes you just need a hug, especially from a furry friend. Miles knew, but he didn't have to tell me. It's the twin thing.

Chapter 6 - The Salty New Year

It was the next day before I realized I had not really helped Miles much with the planning. When I was outside with Pepper, Scott stuck his head out the door and said he had ordered take-out and we needed to go pick it up. I sent Miles a text the next morning, feeling bad about being so unhelpful, and for him to let me know what I need to do for the party. He replied with:

All good Mols, Scott and I have it covered

I remembered to ask Scott about it when he got home from work and he just casually shrugged and said, "It's not much, I'm just helping him get some supplies together and delivered."

It felt weird to not be involved in planning something; no supplies to pick up, no arrangements to make, no food to bring. In a way, I was glad, because my heart still wasn't in it and I didn't really want to go.

Nobody told me that the people I loved the most, who loved me the most, were planning the most perfect New Year's celebration, all for me. A tradition we would continue for many, many years.

***

On New Year's Eve, I woke early, tiptoeing out of the room so I didn't wake Scott. I was sitting at the table drinking my coffee in the dark when I heard the sound of singing upstairs, it got louder and louder. Jason appeared, bags looped around his arms, carrying two boxes. He had his headphones in and was singing along to *Circles* by *Post Malone*. He didn't see me. He set the boxes down and headed back up. When he returned he had two more boxes. He set them down and when he stood back up he got serious. He held a party favor up to his mouth and sang the chorus at the top of his lungs.

I wished so badly I had been recording this, but I knew better. I took a video of both kids dancing to *The Spice Girls* while playing Just Dance on the Wii and they were horrified and made me delete it. Nobody told them nothing is ever really deleted. Not for moms. I put my hand over my mouth to try not to laugh, both at the impromptu breakfast concert and also the secret video I've seen about 200 times. My movement caught his eye and he whipped around. His face was a shade of red I hadn't seen before. "You scared me, mom!"

I figured he didn't want me to dissect his vocal performance, so I took off my Simon Cowell hat and changed the subject quickly. "What's all that stuff for?"

Before he could answer, the front door flew open and Miles and Scott walked in. I wasn't even aware that Scott was awake, let alone out of the house.

Without even a glance in my direction, the boys went to work.

"Let's load 'em up! The truck's out front and ready to go." Miles yelled.

Scott flew past me up the stairs. "Where's Avery?" He shouted.

"You know Avery, she just takes for-" Jason started to say.

"I'M COMING, GOD; DON'T RUSH ME." Avery's voice boomed down from the second floor.

Scott rushed back down the stairs. "Where're the boxes I brought home on Monday? They're not in the closet anymore."

"They're already at the Dog," Jason called over his shoulder. "I couldn't find a good place to put them, and I needed the closet space to hang my clothes."

Miles popped his head back in the door. "Is Pepper in here? Shit. Avery, go find Pepper! I think she chased some birds down the street."

"Can we stop and get coffee on the way?" Avery asked on her way out the door to find Pepper.

Jason passed her in the door. "Get some here, before we leave."

"It's not the same, I want the good stuff from the drive-thru one by the Dog." She shouted from the street. I could barely hear her, but she was probably waking everyone on the block.

Miles, loading boxes in his truck, shouted back in an equally neighbor-waking tone, "You can walk over when we get there."

"But it's a drive-thru, not a walk-thru," She yelled back.

Miles, still forgetting that the Fowlers lived in a neighborhood, hollered out, "We're all loaded up, let's get out of here."

The wild display in front of me was confusing and chaotic. I was unsure what was happening. I felt like I was watching an agitated ant hill. Nearly nobody had even noticed me, other than startling Jason. Was I invisible? Scott, almost as if he heard my thoughts, opened the door and headed straight for the table, a big smile on his face and an envelope in his hand. He kissed me long and hard and handed me the stiff white rectangle and said, "I love you, see you tonight."

"Wait!" I called out. "What's going-" The door shut behind him, cutting off my sentence. I looked down at the envelope. On the outside, it said *Be at the Dog at 7:00 p.m. We will meet you there. Enjoy this day, we love you.* Scott, Avery, Jason, and Hannah all signed their names on the front. On the right, in familiar block writing, it said *They made me sign this, Miles.*

The envelope was full of gift cards: The spa, bookstore, coffee shop, clothing store, lunch. My eyes were blurred with tears. There was a little note inside the envelope written in Scott's writing. *These are yours, please don't use them to buy books and clothes for the kids, and don't give the coffee one to Avery. These are yours.* I smiled. He knew me so well because that's exactly what I would do. That's exactly what I did.

I showered and dressed for the day, feeling excitement and anticipation for the day that I had not expected. I couldn't stop smiling. I settled into the car, ready for relaxation, shopping, and time for me. Just before I pressed the ignition button I paused and took note of the silence. It was clear that I would have to get used to this, a quiet car. When the kids were little I cherished these moments when I could go off by myself, a run to the grocery store alone, a trip to the library or coffee shop without two kids in tow. Nobody told me that someday I would miss it.

Each of my kids had their own unique *car personality*, as I liked to call it. Avery absolutely had to control the music and would accept no alternative. Jason loved to talk in the car. He was normally a quiet and reserved kid, but when the vehicle was in motion, it was open mic night. As you could imagine, these two *car personalities* were not compatible. The two of them had always been close and rarely fought, but as soon as the car door shut, it was a combat zone.

I pulled the envelope out of my purse and looked again at the gift cards inside, planning my day and which stops I would make first. The gift card for *Beans by the Bay* was discreetly tucked back into my purse. Of course, I would give it to Avery. She liked to go there after school and she'd never tell Scott if it meant free coffee. I took out the card for the spa and also tucked that one away. I couldn't pamper myself all day, that was the ultimate in selfish behavior. I would save that for a day when Avery and I could do that together, or maybe she and Hannah could have a fun day together. The gift card for the clothing shop was removed and stuffed into my wallet. I was definitely going to use that one. I considered the lunch and bookstore cards. I didn't really need to eat out when I had plenty of food here at the house. I stuck the lunch card behind the spa card. I felt those two went well together. No need to do those today by myself. The bookstore card was tempting. There was a new book released recently by my favorite author. I also remembered Avery talking about a leatherbound monogrammed journal and fountain pen she saw there that she just had to have. I would go to the bookstore and the clothing store, come back home and eat my lunch and get ready for the party. I smiled and started the car, satisfied with my plans.

When I arrived at the Dog at 7:00 p.m. there were already cars lined up and down the block. I stuffed the bag of books and journals for Avery in the backseat along with the cute dress I bought for her. I also found a leather jacket for Jason that would look great on him. He's more likely to snitch on me, so I'd give it to him another day when it looked less obvious when I bought it.

On the sidewalk in front of the Dog was a whiteboard that listed the instructions next to a table that held folded T-shirts in piles based on color. Hannah stood behind the table wearing a pink shirt, beaming. I waved and smiled and stopped to read the sign.

Are you looking for good fortune in the New Year? At the First Annual Salty New Year, you can stack the deck with various good luck traditions from around the world (modified for time and supplies)

1. *Perform any and all traditions as instructed at the Luck Stations around the room.*
2. *At the top of each hour from 9 to midnight, a group event will take place.*

I was speechless. I turned toward Hannah. She explained the purpose of the T-shirts, what each color represented, and that you choose the shirt to wear based on what you're hoping for most in the coming year. She went on also to explain that traditionally it's supposed to be the color of your underwear, but Miles said he didn't want to see anybody's underwear, especially his sister's. She giggled at that. I picked a white T-shirt from the pile. Happiness. I smiled again at Hannah in her pink shirt, Love and Harmony.

Inside the Dog, the tables were lined up around the room. The first one had small bags filled with lentils. I was told by Kara, one of the waitresses at the Dog, that in Columbia they carry them in their pocket all night. My jeans were a little snug but I managed to make them fit.

The final table had baskets of flowers and a small children's pool filled with water. Brandon, our paperboy, stood next to the pool and explained that in Brazil they throw flowers in the ocean at midnight. This wasn't the ocean and it wasn't midnight, but it was the next best thing. I picked up a handful and threw them in and smiled. This was exactly what I needed, to stack the deck, give me hope.

He had also scheduled *Top of the Hour* traditions. These were a huge hit amongst the large crowd. He saved our local midnight hour for the traditional one, the actual countdown and midnight kiss.

At 9:00 everyone carried a miniature paper suitcase in one hand and a dollar bill in the other and ran around the block. This was also a Colombian tradition. Well, sort of. It was to bring fortune and money in the new year. It wasn't my priority, but I wasn't about to skimp on anything.

At 10:00 we were all instructed to stand on a chair and jump off at the end of the countdown to leap in the New Year as they do in Denmark. Miles had very strict warnings about this and waivers had to be signed before a chair was provided. He was always a cautious business owner. His insurance agent would be proud.

Just before the 11:00 hour, plastic cups holding 12 grapes each were handed out to the guests. On the stage Miles explained how this tradition worked in Spain, that they eat a grape at each stroke of midnight; one grape for one month of good luck in each of the coming 12 months. A video was played on the big screen that Miles explained is shown in Spain every year, hence the Spanish countdown. Scott and I stood next to each other, popping each grape into our mouths one by one, our eyes dancing with silent laughter as we tried to swallow each grape as fast as possible.

He leaned in for the kiss after the final grape was consumed, and the sweet, fruity taste on our lips reminded me of the ridiculously expensive wine we bought for our wedding night, a bottle of which we kept in the cupboard to share on our 25th anniversary next year. I felt a peace that we were going to be okay because our life together was like a fine wine, it just got better with age.

I looked forward to twelve months of good luck and happiness in the coming year. Nobody told me I dropped three grapes.

CHAPTER 7 – THE FLIP OF THE CALENDAR

I walked into my office on a beautiful morning in February and set my coffee on my desk. I was in a great mood that morning. The weather was nice, the birds were singing. Scott had placed a birdbath and feeder in the yard and they were happily splashing and enjoying breakfast.

Scott's birthday was Friday and the four of us had taken a road trip to Portland to see *Chris Stapleton*. We stayed overnight and then went to the coast the next day and stayed two nights in a cabin on the ocean in Seaview. It was magical. These little mini-vacations were the links in our family chain. I treasured them. I placed the new picture frame I purchased in Seaview up on the wall. The picture inside the frame was taken of the four at the arena just before the show started. I smiled. Another happy memory. My smile faded as I wondered how many more concerts we would attend together. Probably none. This may have been the last.

I shook my head to clear the negative thoughts. *Enjoy the beautiful day, Molly, don't ruin it.* I watched some birds out the window and realized we were getting close to spring. Winter was in our rearview mirror. Temperatures in the Northwest rarely dropped even close to Midwest numbers, but there was something depressing about the gray skies, darker days, and days upon days of rainy weather.

We did get the occasional snowstorm here, and because it was so rare it was usually treated like a holiday. It definitely was in the Fowler house. We all took the day off, regardless of the status of school and work closures. We brought out the sleds, we had snowball fights, and we built snowmen. Then we would come inside and have hot chocolate and play games. No matter how old the kids got, we always had the best time playing in the snow together.

Our favorite snow days were when they started in the evening and continued through the night. If someone woke up to snow blanketing the ground, no matter what time it was we all bundled up in our winter gear and took a middle of the night walk in the snow. Snowy, dark nights are so enchanting. There is something magical about walking down dark, empty, unusually soundless streets, except for Avery screaming when her brother put a snowball down her coat. I laughed out loud at that memory. I recalled with sadness that we didn't get any snow this past winter.

Nobody told me that last year when we took our midnight snow walk, when I wanted to go back early because I was too cold and tired, that it was probably the last one we would ever take. Nobody told me how much I would regret that. Why was I so selfish? Stay outside, throw snowballs, laugh with your kids, make a snowman, ride the sled, lay on the cold ground, and make a snow angel. The warm house will always be there, but these moments will not. Regret.

I turned back to my laptop, less enthusiastic than I was earlier. I had a tendency to bring my own mood down pretty quickly. I was becoming my own worst enemy. I checked my emails, responded to clients, booked appointments, as well as responded to requests for meetings and showings.

An email from my boss, Gordon, had the subject line *March Meeting today at 1:00*. The email message went on to outline what would happen at this meeting.

On the first business day of every month, all agents were required to attend a meeting in the office to discuss monthly goals, results of the previous month, etc. I laughed at Gordon. He was a day early. I hit reply and began to type. As I did my eyes darted briefly to the lower right corner of my laptop screen. The date said March 1st. *No.* I picked up my phone and looked at the date on the screen. March 1st. *No. No.* I thought back and remembered suddenly that although we had gone to the concert on Friday and celebrated Scott's birthday that night, his actual birthday was Thursday. This meant that today was not the 28th of February, but the 1st of March. I closed my eyes and groaned. *March.*

I stood and reached for the calendar on my wall. I flipped the page up. I watched the month of February as it passed by my eyes, pinned to the top, gone forever. February had been uneventful, mostly blank other than Scott's birthday and the concert. The month of March was also blank, uneventful. Except for one day. The last day of the month. It was written in red marker in Avery's handwriting. Big block letters. It was circled multiple times.

IVY DAY

I stopped breathing. I didn't want to see those red letters. I knew it was just a day, just a step in the process. Just a decision. Just a word. Unavoidable.

The pieces of me that were already cracking and threatening to fall apart would find themselves holding on for dear life after the word is read out loud.

Because once this decision is released, the avalanche will start and I won't be able to outrun it.

Without hesitation, if I'm given the choice of seeing my child hurt or being hurt myself, I would always choose the latter. I can heal. I can survive. I can protect them by taking their pain. I wasn't sure I could this time.

Nobody told me that I would survive all of this, that my life will change but it will still go on, the world will still turn, that my life and their lives, in the end, will be better than ever. If they had, I may have handled things differently; I may have been a better mother in the coming months, a better wife, a better person.

CHAPTER 8 - THE DREADED IVY DAY

It was a beautiful day, not the ominous gray skies and thunder I had expected to find on the morning of a day I dreaded so much. A day that would include the first steps in planning to send my youngest child somewhere far away; knowledge of exactly which university was going to steal my daughter.

Avery was already a bundle of nerves, so we knew today was going to have to be about distractions. Even though she had already been accepted to many other colleges, some with very generous merit scholarships, she wouldn't even entertain the fact that she may have to go to a college that wasn't Columbia. Scott put his foot down on applying to more than one Ivy League because of the application cost. He insisted that she apply to the University of Washington. He attended there, Jason and Hannah both attended there as well. He was holding on to the hope that she would attend there as well, follow Jason's path, follow his path. Stay home. Our girl has dreamt of traveling the world and conquering it since she could talk, she was not going to settle for a state college so close to her hometown.

We let her skip school that day. I wanted to ease her anxiety, so I took away all electronics and Hannah and I whisked her away for a day of pampering and shopping. We got massages, facials, manicures, pedicures, waxing, anything she wanted. She tried on clothes for an hour and a half and I put a sizable dent in our credit card. I could see the anxiety still on her face, but she did manage to relax and have a good time.

I noticed something different in Hannah, though. She was quieter than usual. She laughed, but not as much as usual. Her smile wasn't quite as bright. She was distracted. She was very much a part of our family and had been for so long that any small change in her behavior was easily detectable. I could tell something was wrong. I didn't want to pry. It wasn't my place and it wasn't the time. Even if she did confide in me, if it was a problem with Jason, I would have to step back. That wasn't any of my business. No matter how much I cared for her and felt motherly toward her, she wasn't my daughter, but he was my son, and I knew my place.

We were waiting for Avery outside the bathroom at the mall when I noticed Hannah secretly checking her phone. I leaned in to whisper "Don't let Avery see that, she'll rip it out of your hands and run." Hannah laughed but remained silent. It was good to see a genuine smile. "She thinks her odds get better every time she checks the portal."

Hannah laughed again. "As if she needs any more advantages, she's going to Columbia, everyone knows that." My heart sank. I've been avoiding those four words, *she's going to Columbia*, since October. It was like a dog whistle, they kept saying it, but I couldn't hear it. I heard it now. I'd been spinning this fairy tale that she wouldn't get in, that she would be denied and we would just deal with the aftermath and move on. When I woke up that morning I selfishly told myself I'd be comforting my child later, trying to heal her broken heart with my false empathy, then happily prepare her for a college she didn't want to attend, one that was closer to home; a college I wanted her to attend for selfish reasons. That didn't feel right either, but I was becoming more comfortable with my selfish side. I didn't like that, but I didn't like the alternative either.

Avery emerged from the bathroom and we headed out to the car. The final leg of the journey was home. We planned to sit as a family and receive the decision together, good or bad.

As we pulled into the driveway, I saw that both Miles and Jason's cars were already there, as well as Scott's. Avery jumped out of the car and ran into the house. As I pulled the bags from the trunk I noticed Hannah already halfway to her car. She called over her shoulder, "Um…I'm actually going to just head home if that's okay." She opened the door and slid in. "Just tell Avery to text me later." Just before she shut the door she added, "Columbia would stupid not to admit a future Supreme Court Justice. Or maybe she'll cure cancer. Probably both, honestly. Tell her that I said goodbye and that I love her." She said *HER*, not Jason. Before I could process that and respond, she was down the street and gone. I looked at the house and then back at the empty street again unsure of what exactly just happened.

***

There were already several boxes of pizza on the table. A laptop was set up as well, ready for *Operation Columbia Acceptance*. Jason had written those words on a sign and hung it on the wall. I didn't like the word *acceptance*, and I told him it should say *decision*, just in case, but I couldn't convince Avery's biggest supporter that acceptance wasn't guaranteed. I was greeted at the door by a big golden retriever. "Sargent Pepper!" I dropped my bags and prepared to receive her sweet doggy kisses. Miles didn't go a lot of places without his best friend, and she was always welcome in our home.

Avery and Scott were arguing about the laptop. He was telling her she was not to touch it, that it was absolutely off-limits along with all other forms of technology. He had put every phone, iPad, and laptop in the house in a box on the table. Jason handed me a beer and a piece of Hawaiian pizza, my favorite. "What's with Hannah?" I asked. "She was acting weird today, did you two have a fight?" He just shrugged and went back to assisting Scott in keeping Avery away from the table. It did look like a two-person job, but I was pretty sure he was just dodging the question. None of this felt right, but it wasn't the time to press, and it wasn't my business. That's a later problem if he wanted to talk about it. Today was Avery's day. I watched him walk across the living room and wrap his arms around his sister, physically restraining her from touching the forbidden object. She giggled. He got very serious. "I'll tie you to the chair if I have to, Avery!" The amount of laughter this house has seen over the years could fill an entire universe.

I walked over to the couch where Miles was feeding Pepper a piece of pizza. "If you want Pepper to live long enough to be your retirement buddy, you might want to think about feeding her certified dog food."

He scoffed. "That stuff is disgusting. She deserves the same luxuries that I do, maybe more." Miles never had children or got married. He had devoted his life to his business, but Pepper was his baby. I couldn't argue with him. *Let her eat the pizza.*

"Have you made any more retirement plans?" I sat next to him and started eating my own pizza, trying to ignore the begging dog at my knee. Miles had made the decision a few months ago to start the process of retiring. He was only 45, but had built quite an empire with The Salty Dog franchise and had worked his ass off to get there. He asked Jason to come work for him, to eventually take over the business, which he accepted. The Uncle Miles Hat Trick.

"It's only a semi-retirement, Mols" he reminded me "and it's still quite a ways off, Jason doesn't even graduate until June. But yes, I have." He smiled. "I bought an RV last week. Pepper and I are going to travel in style." He pulled his phone out to show me some pictures. It was absolutely gorgeous, top of the line.

"Damn, Milo, maybe I'll retire with you." I handed his phone back to him.

"Absolutely not." He said. "If I had to travel the country with you I might push you into the Grand Canyon."

"No need, I would jump voluntarily." I grabbed the plates and headed toward the kitchen. "Between you and Pepper, that RV is going to smell like a fart factory."

"It's time!" Scott announced. He had blindfolded Avery and sat her on a chair at the table with the laptop in front of her. The plan was to have the decision up before we removed the blindfold. It would take several attempts at refreshing the screen before a decision was posted. She was getting impatient. Jason and Miles were taunting her. They were making dramatic sounds as if they were shocked by the results. She was like a rabid dog tied to a post. My stomach was in knots.

Scott refreshed the Columbia portal one final time.

Accepted.

I had unnecessarily prepared to console her. I was the one who needed the comforting now, and nobody prepared for that. Once the curtain of delusion I hung was ripped down, I could admit to myself that I wasn't surprised by the news. I always knew. I heard the dog whistle, I just ignored it. Now it was deafening.

My eyes blurred with tears, happy tears, sad tears, excited tears, proud tears, scared tears. Through them, I saw Scott smile at me. I saw all of my emotions and feelings reflected back at me. We had spoken very little about this moment and what it was going to mean for our family. How it would change us. We should have.

Avery's blindfold came off, and so did mine. Everything I had avoided was suddenly there in front of me. Nobody told me that my daughter's happiness could make me so damn sad.

CHAPTER 9 – THE TRAIN WRECK

Spring break came the week after the Columbia news shook our house. Jason and Hannah had planned to spend a few days in Vancouver, Canada during that time. I secretly hoped that he had a ring packed in his suitcase, but after the weird behavior they both exhibited on Ivy Day, I wasn't sure anymore. Now I just hoped they could get over whatever was troubling them. For a mom who takes pride in avoiding any unwanted involvement in her children's love lives, I certainly get entirely too nosy in my imaginary world to make up for it.

As it turned out, the trip was still scheduled and they were due to leave Sunday afternoon and stay until Thursday. On Sunday morning at breakfast, Jason asked Avery if she'd like to join them. He told her he and Hannah wanted to take her to celebrate her Columbia admission. This was very unsettling to me. All of my made-up scenarios of Hannah and Jason's trip went up in flames. What about the proposal? I wanted to plan a wedding, a happy occasion. Clearly that wasn't Jason's plan if he's inviting his sister. And they can't take Avery, she's too young to go that far without me. And lastly, and most important of all, nobody thought to ask me. I'm still her mother.

Avery was thrilled with the invitation. Before I could even blink she announced that she was going to pack her bag and ran for the stairs. Everything was spiraling. My ears were ringing with what I assumed were alarm bells. Alarm bells that told me that I needed to stop this. They can't take her. She can't go. They changed their plans. They're taking my baby. No. Nobody told me the alarm bells were a warning that I was about to make a colossal mistake.

"Hold on a second!" I yelled a little louder than I should have. Anger probably wasn't necessary at the moment, but I was furious and I couldn't stop it. Most of my frustration was fueled by the complete loss of control I felt in my life; I knew I was misdirecting it, but the train was out of control, about to derail. "You didn't even ask for my permission. You can't just decide that you want to go, pack your clothes, and leave without even speaking to me first."

Damn it, Molly, you're not this kind of mother. Stop.

I didn't stop.

Avery and Jason stared at me, confusion all over their faces. They didn't recognize this woman. In the space of time, before any of us could speak again, Scott came down the stairs. He apparently only heard a part of our conversation because he said, "Permission for what?"

Avery was the first to speak; knowing her father was her superhero, her defender, she said, "Jason asked me to go to Canada with them to celebrate my Columbia admission and Mom said no." She wasn't really the type to use her dad to get her way, and she probably wasn't now either, and I'm almost certainly remembering that sentence incorrectly, but it felt that way to me. A conspiracy. An attack.

I groaned. "I did not say no, Avery, I said you didn't ask my permission."

Scott kissed Avery's forehead and rumpled her hair. "Of course you can go, have a blast." He pulled out his wallet and handed Avery a stack of bills. She squealed and hugged him and ran up the stairs.

Jason worriedly looked at his dad and then at me and made the smart decision to leave the room, fast. As he was heading up the stairs he yelled, "Avery make it snappy, we're leaving in 10 minutes." I didn't hear what she said, but I heard what he said next. "Yea, well I think it's probably smart if we head out now, take the emergency exit." He was referring to us. He was referring to me.

Scott didn't seem to notice the raging volcano that his wife had become and the imminent eruption. He placed his wallet back in his pocket and walked into the kitchen. He poured some coffee into his favorite mug. Avery bought it for him, it said *Best Dad Ever*. I wanted to throw it across the room. Shatter it. He had not even looked at me since he betrayed me, dismissed me, overruled my parental authority.

"That was so nice of them to invite her! Now we can have some alone time for a few days, get a preview of what our life will be like when - " I wouldn't let him finish that sentence.

"Why the hell did you do that? Why did you say yes? How could you let her go?" The fury in me was big and loud and I couldn't control it.

"Why would you say no?" He looked bewildered and walked right past me to the table and set his coffee down. "What's the big deal?"

"Because it's a long way to go and she's only 16, Scott. Canada is an entirely different country. What if something happens? You can't just override my decision like that." As the words exploded out of my mouth I knew they were ludicrous, that I was fighting the wrong battle. I couldn't stop them.

"Molly, she's about to go to college. In six months she will be able to get in a car with her college friends that you've never even met before, maybe never even knew existed, and drive all the way up to Canada and stay as many days as she wants, and not only does she not have to ask your permission, she doesn't even have to tell you." He directed his attention back to his phone, dismissing the argument. This didn't help. Now I was anxious about college again. He looked back up and added, "And I didn't override you, you even said that you didn't say no."

"But I was going to!" I shouted.

He laughed and looked up from his phone. "So, I overruled your decision to say no, by saying yes first? Are you saying that you're the parent that gets to make all the decisions in this house? That I should always consult you first? That I should find out if you want to say *yes* or no *so* I can back you up? You can't change the rules of the game in the bottom of the 9th."

I hated the way he said that, the way he made me feel like the bad guy, the way he compared it to baseball, the way he called it the bottom of the 9th. The end. I stormed out. I wanted to yell, but I didn't want the kids to leave for Canada while their parents were fighting. I didn't want them to go at all. I hated Canada. I turned and stomped toward the door.

I planned to get in my car and drive away, anywhere, but before I started the car I saw the front door open. Avery and Jason stepped onto the porch, suitcases in hand. They both paused when they saw me in the car. Damn. I was going to leave without saying goodbye. How selfish was that? This wasn't fair to them. I wanted to be mad, I felt like I deserved it. I felt justified in my anger. But I didn't know exactly who I was angry at. It wasn't Avery. It wasn't Jason. They didn't deserve this. I realized it also wasn't Scott. He also didn't deserve this. I was angry at myself. I was losing control of my life, but instead of steering into the skid I'm fighting it. I was going to crash if I wasn't careful.

I stepped out of the car and Avery came to me and wrapped me in a tight hug. "I'm sorry, Mom, I know you probably had made plans for us this week and I ruined them. Can we reschedule when I get back?"

I didn't specifically plan anything, which made me feel worse. I should have. She was assuming I didn't want her to go because I wanted her to stay, spend time with me. "Of course we can, sweetie," I lied and averted my eyes. I'll change the plans and we will have a great weekend together." And we would. A really great weekend. The best. She beamed.

Jason came over and hugged me and said, "I'll take care of her, Mom, I promise." He flashed a smile at me. At the last second he leaned in and whispered, "Give Dad a break, Mom, you're both having a difficult time, arguing isn't going to help." I smiled. He never got involved in any disagreement between Scott and I. He never took sides. I felt like I probably should be taking that to heart, both the fact that this isn't something he normally would do or say, but the fact that he was right.

I watched his car disappear down the street and turned toward the house. Our house. Our home. I went inside, planning to give the man who had given me his whole heart, his whole life, the honor of raising his children, a very sincere apology. I was wrong, and I admitted it. The guilt was overwhelming. I yelled at Scott. I made Avery feel bad for wanting to leave. I made Jason feel guilty for inviting her. I just kept fucking up. I wish I could say right now that nobody told me I'd fuck up so much, but someone did. I did.

I stepped back into the house and sat next to Scott at the table. He didn't look up from his phone. I wanted to apologize, tell him I wasn't sure what happened, why I did that, why I said that. I wasn't even entirely clear why I didn't want her to go. I should have said, *of course, have a great time!* Then I would have been able to enjoy a few days with Scott, go out to dinner, see a movie, maybe even play a couple of rounds of cribbage. Instead, I started this course of a train wreck that I couldn't stop. This week would have been amazing, for us, for the kids, but I ruined it. Scott was going to be on edge, wondering what happened to his wife, whether she would snap again. The kids were probably going to be worried about us, whether we were arguing or not.

Before I could say anything he set his phone down and said,"I was thinking maybe we could go out to that new Mexican restaurant that just opened tonight, what do you think? I love the name, *Tequila Mockingbird*." He chuckled and stood up, bringing his mug to the sink.

He put his own olive branch out by not discussing the morning's events. I appreciated it, but also I kind of wanted to tell him how I felt, tell him about the pit in my stomach and the ringing in my ears that wouldn't stop. I wasn't sure if his quick dismissal of the whole morning was his way of telling me it's okay and that he understood what I was going through, or that he just wasn't ready to address it. Now would have been a good time for him to grab me by the shoulders and tell me that I was completely off the rails. But nobody told me. Nobody.

CHAPTER 10 - THE DINNER

The housing market had picked up finally and I was selling houses like crazy. I found myself working more than I should, weekends and evenings. I was able to justify working so much because I knew that every dime from the commissions were going into Avery's Columbia tuition account. The school wasn't cheap, and although she had applied for scholarships, nothing was guaranteed. The guilt over being away from my family so much at this time was always hanging over me, but for the first time, I felt like Scott was proud of the contribution I was making and wasn't looking at my work as just something I do to pass the time.

My job as a real estate agent was not necessary for our household budget. Scott had long called it my *Vacation Occupation*, which was funny at first but the longer I did it the more I loved it and felt like his comments were dismissing my career as something that was frivolous, a joke. I resented that, but when I am in a position to provide fun things like family vacations, cars for Avery and Jason on their birthdays, and now college tuition, it felt good, I felt like a fundamental part of the family. When I place a family into their dream home, I feel very proud of the part I play in making someone's dreams come true.

I was finalizing some paperwork on another big sale when a text from Jason came in.

Will everyone be at dinner tonight?

As far as I know, why?

Wanted to discuss something.

OK see you tonight.

This gave me hope. Two weeks had passed since the trip to Canada and Ivy Day. The three of them seemed to have a good time. There was no proposal. Since they all came back Hannah had not been around much. I wondered though, against my better judgment and inner agreement to mind my own business, if she felt Jason was dragging his feet about the proposal. The crossroads of finishing college and starting your adult life is a big deal for anyone, but for a woman who had spent six years with the same boy, watched him become a man, she had to feel like she needed more: A ring, a house, a family, a future. I might be wrong, because like I said, it's none of my business. I couldn't help but think that a wedding, especially a summer wedding, would take my mind off the spiraling disaster I've become. It would have to be put together quickly, but perhaps wedding planning would center me, make me remember the woman I used to be, the mom I'm supposed to be. Maybe this family meeting would include an announcement that doesn't contribute to my mental collapse.

I made a list of ingredients for dinner. I ordered them online to be delivered this afternoon. I developed a hatred for public places lately. Everyone wanted to talk about Avery's news. I was very proud and excited for her, but there were days when I couldn't get past the fact that my daughter will have just turned 17 when she packs her bags and moves almost 3,000 miles away from me. I should have had another year to prepare. I would have been ready by then, not so sad, more excited. I wouldn't have to cry in the shower, because my tears would be for joy and pride, not sadness and fear. Not guilt and selfishness. Not self-loathing. I was mad at the whole world, but when people in town wanted to talk about it, rave about it, I became mad at them as if it were their fault. I kept the anger hidden though. I didn't dare tell a soul. I was aware I was being selfish, and now was not the time to wear that crown publicly.

I sent Scott a text and told him that Jason had something to discuss at dinner and asked him to pick up a bottle of champagne.

You think this is the big one?

Idk maybe, hopefully. I don't want to get my hopes up, but I do want some bubbly :)

You got it, love you Mols.

Avery got home around the same time the groceries arrived. "Did you seriously order grocery delivery? The store is three miles from here." She carried them in the house and set them down. "You used to make fun of people who did that."

"Don't judge me until you're an adult with a family and a job and find out how much work it can be to just get to the store; delivery is a godsend." I began the process of marinating the steaks.

Avery lingered in the kitchen for a while, not really speaking, but not leaving. I figured she had something on her mind. I waited for her to open up, ready to help solve her dilemma.

"So, I have some news," She said quietly. The knots in my stomach tightened. *Oh no.* This wasn't going to be a problem for Mom to solve, it's going to just be another problem *for* Mom. *Another one.* How much more could I take? Graduation. Columbia. Jason's big news. Now this. I stopped peeling the carrot. "I know Jason has something to share, would it be okay if I did too? Or is that too much?"

It was too much. I wanted to tell her to wait until tomorrow, and then the next day, and then the next day.

Scott arrived home and handed me the champagne. "Avery has some news too, Scott," I blurted out as I put it on ice. I threw the curveball at him, hoping he would say *stop with the news, stop hurting us, stop making your mother cry.*

"What is it?" He said as he looked at Avery, expertly dodging my curveball. He looked intrigued, excited almost. *Dammit.* Why am I always afraid of what's next, while he's excited? Am I the wrong one, should I put my feelings aside and just be happy for whatever it is? Or is he wrong? Maybe he's not really excited, maybe he's just a really good actor and is dying inside. Maybe not showing Avery his true feelings is making him a better parent. Maybe he's just stronger than I am.

She looked to me for approval to break the news. It didn't matter when she said it, it was going to happen, might as well be now. I shrugged, defeated. I held my breath waiting for the next devastation.

"I got a scholarship. A full 4-year one, exclusive to Columbia." I let my air out. That was easy. Scott's excitement was over the top.

I managed a hug and said, "Congratulations." Then I stepped outside for air. I wasn't used to getting news that didn't rock me to my core and I seemed to forget how to show genuine positive emotions; how to shift gears from dread to happiness. Probably because of the nagging feeling in my gut. I closed my eyes and told myself I needed to stop being so foolish. I was truly excited for her, but I couldn't help but feel suddenly so useless again. All the commission I earned was for nothing. I worked all those long hours, putting check after check into an account, feeling more and more satisfied with myself as that number grew, knowing that one day I'd give it to Avery for her future. I missed dinners, movies, even a concert we had planned to attend together. They had to go without me, Hannah took my spot. All of this was time I couldn't get back. The thing that bothered me the most with this scholarship was the thought that she could and probably would spend the next 4 years there. Until that moment I had held out a sliver of hope that she would change her mind and transfer somewhere closer. A full 4-year ride to Columbia is a pretty good reason to stay there.

I heard Jason's car in the driveway, so I went back inside to get ready for dinner. Scott was already outside grilling. It was a beautiful spring day in April, but there was still a little chill in the air, so I brought him a jacket. He thanked me. "Can you believe this? A full 4-year scholarship?" He laughed to himself and shook his head. "This would only happen to Avery, the girl with the golden touch." He flipped the steaks.

I watched Jason and Avery through the sliding glass door. I couldn't hear what they were saying, but she was clearly giving him her news. I didn't want her to take away his spotlight, but Jason would never have cared. He loved his sister and was so proud of her. He hugged her and they talked animatedly for a few minutes. They've always been so supportive of each other. I saw Jason was speaking now for a few minutes and whatever he said made Avery very excited and they ran upstairs together, laughing. After witnessing that wordless exchange, I smiled to myself. It has to be the engagement announcement, and he wanted to tell his sister first. Avery would be ecstatic about this news and Jason had always said he would ask Avery to be his 'best woman', so maybe that's what he did now before he formally announced it.

I put my arm through Scott's, feeling content and happy for a moment with the fantasy I created in my head, a situation I could control, a time where I didn't feel like I was drowning. I put the previous thought of feeling useless and all the lost moments away for now so I could truly enjoy this feeling, despite how fabricated it was.

"Earth to Molly.." Scott's voice snapped me out of my daydream. "Where'd you go?" He laughed. "Did you hear what I said?"

"Sorry, no I didn't." I turned to give him my full attention.

"I said you should take a sabbatical from work. You've been working too much lately anyway, you should focus on spending time with Avery before she leaves, preparing for two graduations, and now maybe planning a wedding. I just don't see any reason for you to work right now when your family needs you."

My heart sank. "You want me to quit my job?"

"A sabbatical, Molly, not quit. Just some time off to focus on your family." I was feeling more and more defensive.

"I always put my family first," I snapped. "I was just trying to help pay for Avery's tuition."

"Molly, I know that, which is kind of the point. You don't need to do that anymore. I'm not trying to start a fight; it's just a suggestion." He grabbed the steaks and headed toward the door. He held it open for me, but I hadn't budged an inch. And I didn't plan to. Figuratively anyway, I truly was hungry.

***

After dinner Jason stood up and cleared his throat. "I'm just going to come right out and say it. I've taken a position at a company in New York City that will start in July. It's a company that sells sports energy drinks, hydration products, bodybuilding formulas, that kind of thing. Avery was beaming at her brother. This is why she was so thrilled. Her brother was moving to New York with her. My kids were both moving to New York City. Both of them. *Both.*

Scott jumped to his feet, hugging Jason, offering up his congratulations. Why was he so happy? He wanted our son to move across the country? Jason brought his laptop out and was showing them the company website, places in New York. I still had not moved or said anything. I was unable to.

"I have a question," I said finally. "What about Miles? He thinks you're taking over for him. What about Hannah? Is she moving too? Are you still getting married? I don't understand."

Jason got up and sat next to me. He looked at me and smiled softly. "I told Uncle Miles this morning and he was excited for me and supportive of the idea. As for Hannah, she's not coming. We broke up last week; it was a mutual thing. She's not interested in moving away and I'm not interested in staying. Everything is going to be okay, Mom, I promise." His light brown eyes twinkled with his typical boyish charm. He smiled and laid his hand on my arm. "Who knows what will happen in the future, right? Maybe I'll come back, maybe Hannah will change her mind. I just need to do this for me right now." He leaned in closer to whisper something only I could hear, "I'll always be your sunshine, mom, no matter where I live."

I nodded as if I understood, but I didn't. I leaned in and gave him a hug as tight as I've ever hugged someone. So tight that maybe he wouldn't let go ever. I didn't dare open my eyes because the tears fighting to come out were not of happiness, but sadness, and I felt as if once they started they may never stop.

Nobody told me about this part. The part about how loud the sound of your own heart breaking can be.

Chapter 11 – The Wrath of Molly

After the excitement of the evening died down and the kids retired to their rooms to make plans and tell their friends, Scott sat down in front of the TV and turned on the baseball game. I managed to fake my enthusiasm all evening and not make eye contact with Scott. I was mad. At Scott, at Jason, at New York City, at whoever made these energy drinks, at all the people in the world who drink them, but most especially at Miles. He could have stopped all of this. He should have.

I cleaned up the kitchen and grabbed my purse and keys and headed to the door.

"Where the hell are you going, Molly? It's 9:00. I thought we'd open the champagne and celebrate." I turned slowly from the door to face him. I felt my body start to shake.

"Celebrate what, Scott? The fact that both of our kids are now moving so far away that it will take me a minimum of an entire day to get to them if something happens, or the fact that I just now find out that you think I have spent years focusing more on my career than my family, and that now that they're leaving you to think I should quit and be the mom and wife I should have been all these years?" I watched his face fall, not expecting anything that I just said. He looked shocked.

He responded quickly. That's a bit dramatic, Molly, I didn't mean it that way and you know it, but yes, now would certainly be a good time to take off, especially after Jason's news tonight. Your job has really just been a pastime anyway, wouldn't you rather spend some extra time with me and the kids? Remember, they're leaving in a few months." He flipped the channels, assuming he won the argument.

I brushed off that last comment, not wanting to admit he might be right; I couldn't think about any of that now or make a decision in that regard because I had another mission. A bigger one. "I need to go talk to Miles," I said and opened the door, dismissing this conversation before I let the anger at Miles get misdirected.

He groaned, "Jesus, Molly, don't. It's not his fault, he –" I didn't hear the rest of the sentence and I didn't want to. I slammed the door and got in my car.

***

Miles was already sitting on his porch with Pepper when I pulled into the driveway. Pepper was excited to see me, Miles was not..

"I see Scott warned you I was coming." I slammed the door and marched toward the porch. I followed him into the house, trying to step around Pepper as she eagerly jumped around trying to get my attention.

"He didn't, nor did he have to; I already expected The Wrath of Molly to storm the beaches this evening. You're later than I expected though, I thought you would have been here nanoseconds after the news broke. You want a beer?" He grabbed a Coors Light out of the refrigerator and handed it to me.

"You hate this kind," I pointed out.

"I bought it for you, I figured if you're going to yell at me you might want to wet your whistle a bit first so you don't lose your voice, although Scott might appreciate that."

I hated it when he deflected my seriousness with humor. Typical Miles. "How could you do this to me, Miles?"

He laughed and sat down on a stool at the kitchen counter and crossed his arms. "Which part? The part where I offered your son a job or the part where I was a supportive uncle when he changed his mind? I'm confused on which one you're referring to." He absentmindedly flipped his beer cap into the garbage. He was making light of this situation.

I sat down at the counter and opened my beer. "The part where you let him go back on his word. He took the job and you just let him back out of it. You should have made him stay here." As I said it out loud I started to feel sheepish and selfish and just absolutely fucking crazy.

I laid my head down on my arms and groaned. He sat silent for a minute before he said, "Did you hear what you just said?" I nodded. "I only offered him that job to give you peace of mind after Avery's news. I figured if he accepted it, stayed, and continued to work with me and take over, that would be awesome; as long as he was happy." He paused. "After he accepted it, I hoped that after being faced with an absolute permanent future, staying here, getting married, having kids, he would be able to truly decide if that's what he wanted, and that's what he did, and this isn't it." I lifted my head up and looked at my little brother, wise beyond his years. "He wants to see what else is out there. We didn't get that opportunity." I buried my face again, wishing he hadn't said that last part, a little piece of my life I wanted to stay buried.

He put his hand on the back of my head, a small gesture of comfort between the only other person in the world who knew. He spoke again, yanking me back to the present. "Molly, you have given your kids the confidence to do whatever they want, be whoever they want. Don't stop now. You know he would have done exactly what you wanted him to do, meet all of your expectations, and you would have been thrilled. Would he have been happy? Maybe. Maybe he'll come back and do all of that, but Jason will be happier in the end for making his own decisions, not yours."

I lifted my head again and nodded again without speaking. He stood up and filled a bowl with water and laid it down for Pepper. "You gotta let go, Mols. Your kids are grown up now. Did you even ask Jason why he picked New York? Avery was likely a very big part of the equation; he looks after her like you looked after me, and I love that." I smiled at him. He was right about that. He continued while scratching Pepper's ears, "I happen to know he was looking at a lot of different cities, but they were all on the East Coast. Why? You're probably afraid of the answer." My stomach dropped. He's right; I didn't want to know. I buried my face in my hands, embarrassed.

He stood and went back to the kitchen. "You're a great mom, Molly, but you gotta let go. You have to learn that you are going to need to be a different kind of mom going forward. Who that mom depends on you and them, and you're just going to have to figure that out as you go, but you have to be open-minded and not try to control everything." I heard him sit on the stool next to me and the sound of crackers hitting a plate.

"I came here to yell at you," I mumbled into my hands.

He patted my head. "I know, but I outsmarted you. You're lucky to have me. So why are you mad at Scott?" He fed Pepper some of the crackers.

"How'd you know I was mad at Scott, I thought he didn't call you?" I tried to stop him from feeding the dog the cheese, but he held it out of my reach.

"It's the twin thing, remember? So, what do I need to defend Scott about?"

"He wants me to stop working until the kids leave so I can spend time with them." Again, saying it out loud made me feel stupid.

Miles laughed and set the empty plate in the sink. "Wow, Molly, do you actually think about things before you say them? I don't even have to defend Scott, you can figure that one out on your own. You're making this brotherly advice thing seem effortless." He cleaned the kitchen up and turned off the light. "Are we done with this pathetic fight, or do you want me to keep throwing these truth bombs at you? I can give you some tough love for as long as you want, but I have to get up early to drive down to the Portland Dog tomorrow."

I got up and hugged him tightly. He was the best brother. "Thank you, Miles," I said. "I –" He cut me off and pushed me out the door.

"Go home and apologize to Scott. Also, tell him I'm sorry too."

"For what?" I yelled from the car.

"Because he's married to you." I flipped him off as he shut the front door. I rolled my eyes and drove away laughing.

***

I crawled into bed and curled up next to Scott. "I'm sorry," I whispered, "I'll take some time off." He squeezed my hand and kissed it, a silent acknowledgment. The two of us lay there together silent, not sleeping, both of us with thoughts weighing heavy on our minds and hearts. Nobody told me how important it would be that we share these thoughts, rather than quietly suffer. Nobody told me that silence can be an invisible, toxic gas that slowly poisons you.

CHAPTER 12– THE RIGHT THING

I finished up the listings I already had and accepted no more. I focused on making plans, so many plans: Graduation, ordering graduation announcements, scheduling and planning the parties, dorm supplies, apartment hunting, apartment needs, family events, dinners. Every evening I insisted we sit down and eat dinner together as a family. How many did we have left? I refused to count, but I planned on making them all count.

One morning I was in my office filling out and stacking hundreds of graduation announcements when I heard a notification from my laptop that meant a new message arrived on my work email account. I had not officially worked in two weeks so the majority of those messages were being forwarded to other agents. I was intrigued. Plus my hand was cramping and I was looking for an excuse to take a break.

The email was from my boss, Gordon. A client had specifically requested me as an agent. That wasn't terribly unusual, I was the top agent in the firm three years in a row now, my name as on the top of the list. I almost shut the lid and went back to my stack of envelopes when I saw their budget. I've never sold a house anywhere close to that before. I'd have to show houses in neighborhoods I've never even been to. I swallowed. It's just one client, how long would it take to sell a house to someone with a budget that large? They seemed to know what they wanted, and there were plenty of high-end houses available. I'll just make sure to only work during school hours and nobody will even notice. I glanced at my phone, figuring I should probably call Scott and talk to him first. But do I need his permission? No. I glanced up at the wall and saw the framed index card.

Do what feels right and fuck everyone else

I typed out my reply and shut the laptop. I got up and averted my eyes from the frame. I left the office and shut the door, hiding the evidence of my crime behind the door. I wasn't sure if it felt right yet or not, but I needed to get as far away from that as possible before regret caught up to me.

I went to my closet and pulled out my running shoes. I had not been running in a really long time, but right then I had this urge to run away. From what I wasn't sure. Everything. Nothing. Everyone. Myself.

I was only a few blocks away when I remembered it had been a VERY long time since I ran. Running was always my favorite stress reliever but the tightness in my calves and the burning of my lungs were causing the opposite effect. I quietly chastised myself for thinking I was in better shape, but I pressed on.

After I remembered proper breathing techniques, the air started to return to my lungs again. My legs were still screaming, but I told them to shut up and do their job. When I made it to the park I slowed down to a walking pace. I felt good. No, I felt great. The whole time I did not think about anything except putting one foot in front of the other.

At the park, I saw a woman running toward me. Her blonde ponytail was high and tight, her smile big and bright. *Show off.* I thought. As she approached I realized she was slowing down. *Dammit.* I still couldn't catch my breath and Mary Marathon was going to stop for a chat.

"Hey!" She said, not a single huff or puff coming from her. "Beautiful day to run, isn't it?"

I managed to start breathing steadily enough that she probably wouldn't think about calling 911. "It is," I said. Two words. *Great job, Molly, you have the vocabulary of a 2-year-old.*

"I'm Sophie, by the way," She said, flaunting her ability to speak without struggle.

"Molly," I managed to squeak out.

She went on to tell me she had just moved to the area, was a social worker in Los Angeles for a few years, but had a break up with her boyfriend and wanted a fresh start somewhere new. She said she didn't really like being a social worker, especially in LA where she saw some really bad things, but in a small town, she felt like she was just the bad guy, taking kids away from their parents and most of the time she didn't agree with it. She informed me that she had always wanted to be a chef, that she loved cooking. All of this felt a little too friendly for an early morning sweaty chat with a stranger, but at least it gave me time for my lungs to return to capacity and my legs to uncramp.

I was about to make some excuses about leaving when she asked if I wanted to get a coffee. My hesitation must have been mistaken for confusion because she pointed across the park at a little coffee stand and said, "There's one right over there."

I was having a hard time saying no to this peppy little ball of energy, but now wasn't really a good time for me to be making new friends, and I wasn't just referring to the fact that I smelled like a gym sock. This time she seemed to read my silence accurately. Her smile faded and she stepped back and looked away. She quickly said, "I was being too forward, Molly, I apologize. My boyfr - my ex-boyfriend, Thomas, used to tell me I talk to strangers too much, that I'm too pushy." She kept her eyes on the ground while she spoke as if she had been scolded. "I've been here for two months and I haven't made any friends. It's been really lonely."

I let all of that sink in. I thought about how my kids used to stop strangers on the street and talk to them. I thought about Avery and Jason, each moving across the country alone, trying to make new friends, feeling lonely. I thought about them meeting someone like me, someone who was trying to get out of here as quickly as possible, get away from her, get away from them. My heart broke.

"I'd love a cup of coffee, Sophie," I said with a genuine smile. "I didn't bring my wallet though, so if you buy me a cup of coffee today, I'll buy you one next time." Her face lit up at the words *next time*.

"It's a deal!" She bounced towards me, like a blonde Tigger. Nobody told her she just made friends with Eeyore.

***

After Sophie and I finished our coffee and exchanged phone numbers, I started back towards home, my steps getting lighter and lighter the closer I got. I made some pretty big steps today, physically and figuratively. When I got home Scott was in the driveway washing his truck. He looked at me with confusion and said, "When did you start running again?"

I leaned against his truck, breathing a little heavier than I wanted to, holding my side wishing I didn't look like an amateur. "Today," I said when I finally caught my breath.

"I can tell," Scott said with a laugh and sprayed me with the hose. I picked up the soapy sponge and threw it at him, splattering him with suds. He chased me around the car with the hose. I grabbed the entire bucket and poured it over him. We were both laughing when Avery walked up the driveway with a package.

"Gross you guys, get a room." She went to hand me the box but changed her mind when she saw how wet I was. "It's my cap and gown, I thought you'd want to see it." My heart sank. Real life sometimes hits you like a train. Especially when you've been running from it. Literally.

Scott told Avery to put it in the house and we'd look at it when we came in. He pulled me in for a hug, our wet clothes making a sloshing noise that made us both laugh again. He whispered into my neck, "I know it's happening fast. It will be okay, Molly."

He didn't know that. Graduation was in three weeks. How much longer did we even have left? I didn't say that because I wasn't looking for an answer. He didn't have one and even if he did, I didn't want one. I pulled away, not wanting to talk about it anymore, and went to the porch. I took my wet tennis shoes off and set them out to dry. I couldn't wait to run again tomorrow, run away from this dread I felt right now.

Scott spoke up from behind me, "Let's go away this weekend, the four of us, maybe the ocean?" He was watching me as he rolled the hose up, waiting for an answer.

Just then I remembered the email and the closed office door, the reason I ran in the first place. I debated bringing it up now, but instead, I said, "I'll check into it." He beamed. I forced a smile back.

Two steps forward, three steps back. I thought of all of the things that made me feel good today: The run, meeting Sophie, laughing and playing with Scott, the high-end client requesting me specifically. I stood in the shower and let all of those new feelings wash down the drain and let the guilt set in. I felt guilty for taking on the client and not telling Scott. I felt guilty for making a new friend, Sophie was a really great person and deserved better than me.

I thought about the fun I had outside with Scott. Avery saw that. Maybe she thought we were looking forward to them leaving so we could have fun again. I couldn't remember if we had fun with the kids, or was our fun always without them? We went on vacations sometimes without them. I remember those vacations as being relaxing and we always had a great time. We went on family vacations too, but when I think back on those I remember how stressful they are, packing for four people, arranging and navigating travel, deciding what to do where to eat, satisfying everyone, spending money. Scott and I always ended up arguing about something. Did the kids see us having any fun on those trips, or just the arguments and a stressed-out mother? I slid down the shower wall to the floor and cried. Until that moment I thought I was becoming a selfish mother, but nobody told me that I had been one all along.

CHAPTER 13 - THE GUILT STICKERS

When I emerged from the shower, I tried to dry all that guilt away but it clung to me, like little guilt stickers all over. I called down the stairs to tell Scott to order a pizza. He called back with a little comment that I must be too sore from running to cook dinner. More guilt.

I snuck into my office to check my email, seeing if the client had responded, and they had. They named a few houses they were wanting to see this weekend. They didn't live in the area and would only be here occasionally, and this weekend was one of them. The houses were almost two hours from me. I would be gone most of the weekend. Scott wanted to go away with the kids. I needed to do the right thing. Before I could type out the email, Jason was at my office door asking me to come downstairs, he wanted to show me something. Oh great, more news. This always ends well.

When I entered the living room, Jason had his laptop open and was showing an apartment he found in New York. The landlord was able to show to him this weekend if he could make it to town. He showed us the pictures and it did look nice. I assumed that meant Scott's family getaway was canceled, and I felt guilty about being relieved; it meant I could show the houses.

"Let's all go!" Scott announced. "It will be another Fowler Family Adventure, and we'll get to see our kids' new home!" They all looked at me for approval. I hesitated. I hated the phrase *new home*; this was their home. I thought about the email. I thought about the index card.

Do what feels right and fuck everyone else.

I didn't want to make the smiles on their faces disappear, so I nodded. "Let's go to New York!"

I let the three of them handle the planning of the trip while I sat at my laptop staring at the email from the client. The houses they wanted to see were in the 8-10 million range. Even if I wasn't in it for the money, it was an opportunity that was too good to pass up. I could get my leg into bigger and higher markets. I needed to decide if that was important enough to me. They could go to New York without me. I would probably ruin the trip anyway. I was a selfish mother, and I had a locked and loaded hatred of that stupid city. I picked up a family picture in a frame on my desk. I stared at it. Camping trip. Were we having fun? I remembered that Scott and I argued about the tent, one of the poles was bent because I had stepped on it the year before when we took it down. I forgot to pack the hot dogs, and we had to eat the sandwiches I had made for lunch the next day. Were our smiles genuine or was everyone thinking about how I ruined it. I looked back at the email, all those zeros.

Just then I received a text message. Sophie.

It was so nice meeting you today, Molly, I hope we can hang out again soon!

I thought about ignoring her, ghosting her as the kids called it; it was for her own good. I reminded myself of what she said to me that made me stay for coffee in the first place. Talking to strangers. New to town. Lonely. My kids.

Scott poked his head in my office and told me our flight to New York was Friday night, a red eye leaving at 8:30 p.m. from Seatac. I looked back at the email. I could show them a house Friday afternoon and be back before we leave for the airport. Maybe they would buy it. Maybe New York would be a celebration of a huge commission. I smiled to myself. I began to type.

I hit send, ignoring the sinking feeling in my gut saying I was not doing the right thing. I knew what the important things were and what wasn't, what felt right and what didn't, what was right and what wasn't, but I was ignoring all of it because I was wearing my selfish crown, and I was about to show the whole world.

To make myself feel a little better, I sent a text to Sophie, being careful to match her enthusiasm, faking it but knowing it was the right thing to do.

As I walked out I looked at the frame and realized that whoever wrote that missed a big piece of information. Sometimes more than one thing can *feel* right, but only one thing can *BE* right. Nobody told me that sometimes if you choose what *feels* right, but *isn't* right, you end up fucking yourself.

CHAPTER 14 - THE WRONG THING

Friday morning came and I still hadn't told Scott I had a showing that afternoon before our flight. I was terrified of what he would say, what he would think. He would be so disappointed in me.

I was supposed to meet the client at 1:00 at the house they wanted to see. We were leaving for the airport at 4:00. I had never had a house showing regardless of the outcome, last longer than two hours, which gave me an hour to get home. I'd be home by three, which gave me an hour before everyone else was due home and then another half hour before we left. I could do it. I did not feel confident in that thought.

The home was 45 minutes away and the client was an hour late. Every minute was a bucket of gasoline on the fire of anxiety building in me. At 2:04, after 8 polite texts, 6 voicemails expressing concern, and one answered call telling me they were five minutes out (it was 10), they arrived.

They examined the wood on the porch for 10 minutes. They argued over the color of the foyer rug for eight. We didn't even make it to the second floor until 3:34. At that point, I knew I was done. I interrupted an argument about how many bathrooms the house they saw in March had to excuse myself to make a call.

"Where are you?" Scott answered on the first ring. "The kids and I got home early and are ready to go, we figured we'd stop for dinner on the way."

I closed my eyes and let it out. I told him about the client, the showing. I apologized profusely. I felt the weight of my deception between us. His voice went from excited anticipation of a man ready to go on a family vacation to a man who just learned his wife is a liar. I told him to bring my suitcase and I'd head straight to the airport and meet them there. I promised.

When I hung up and looked back I realized I just lied to them. There's no way I'd make that flight. I let them all down and I lied to my husband. I slowly walked back inside and faced the two people I was beginning to hate, people I chose over the people I love the most in the world, and finish what I started.

I watched their headlights fade and let out a scream. A blood-curdling, soul tearing scream. They hated the house. Three hours we spent and they decided they hated it. It would take me at this time of night on a Friday a minimum of 3 hours to get to the airport. I would never make it. I pounded my fist on the steering wheel and cursed everything, but most especially myself and my selfish choices.

I picked up the phone and FaceTimed Sophie. I barely knew her, but I felt like I needed to talk to someone. It was kind of nice to have a friend.

"MOLLY!" She said, "Why are you just sitting there? Start the fucking car and get to the airport."

I sniffed and smiled, appreciating her enthusiasm and optimism for once. "I'll never make it, it's not worth it." I heard my phone ding underneath my hand and pulled it away. It was an email from Sophie. "Soph - what did you -"

"You may not make this flight, and if you don't there's a Delta one an hour later, non-stop. I bought you a ticket. Get your selfish ass to the airport and find your family. You can pay me back in coffee dates."

"I can't -" I started to say.

"Shut up and drive. And stay on the phone, I wanna hear about your family when you're driving to the airport. Also, then I'll know you actually went." I secured her smiling face in the phone rest on the dash and started the car.

"Are you this good of a friend to everyone?" I asked as I set off down the road.

She stayed quiet for a minute, I wasn't sure she heard me. "I've never had any real friends, Molly."

I smiled at her and said, "Well, I'm honored you chose me."

I did make that flight. Barely. The smile on my family's face as I walked down the aisle eased any anxiety I had about their disappointment in me. I may have disappointed them with my decision to take the client and the poor timing of the showing, but I think I fixed it. Scott squeezed my hand, the kids talked about Jason getting a pat-down in the TSA line, and we discussed the plans in New York for tomorrow. We never discussed what I did. We never discussed why I was late, or that I may not have come at all. We swept it under the rug. It didn't feel right, I felt like I should be apologizing for days, that I should still feel their side glances and disappointment for days, weeks, months. Nobody told me that the only person who was disappointed in me - was me.

Chapter 15 - The Epiphany of New York

I didn't want to go to New York and I had a bad attitude about it, but the minute I saw their faces on the plane my bad attitude put it's parachute on and jumped out. I spent the next several days with a renewed appreciation for my family and for this city that they had fallen in love with and planned to call their home. Scott and I also fell in love with the city. I felt such an amazing sense of peace seeing their faces light up, their excitement over each and every new thing they saw, found, and shared. All the money in the world couldn't buy the experiences we had as a family in New York.

I had worried I would ruin the trip somehow, both with my bad attitude and the fact that I seemed to do that a lot. They were probably expecting it anyway, Mom to get stressed out and snap at them, argue with Scott, just be a downer for everyone. I was sure they saw the selfish, horrible person I had become; that they could see the rotten spot in me that had developed, was spreading; that they could hear that voice in my head that told me I did this, I made all of this happen. They were right to get away from me. I tried to shut that down by reveling in the moment, enjoying what I had and what I saw. The longer we were there the less I felt that way.

I felt a happiness in New York that I hadn't felt in some time. I saw the uncontainable joy on their faces, the eagerness to explore every part of the city, their new stomping grounds. It was contagious. Scott was like a little kid, wanting to see everything and do everything. Avery was so excited to show me the Columbia campus that she actually covered my eyes several times so I could be surprised by something she was particularly thrilled about. Her enthusiasm was infectious.

My New York Epiphany hit at an unexpected moment. We were all standing inside the Butler Library on the Columbia campus. Avery had covered my eyes. Not Scott's, not Jason's - mine. She was so excited to show me this library. Me, her mother, the one who was a horribly selfish person. Or was I? Would she have been so excited to see my eyes when her hands were removed from my face if I were all of those things? Would she have not only included me in her passion but recognized my love of libraries and books as well and shared it with me? No. When her hands were removed, I did see the library, but what I saw first was her eyes, large with wonder and excitement, her face lit up with anticipation and joy. Not at the large ceilings and beautiful architecture of the building, or the high shelves filled with knowledge she couldn't wait to absorb, but she was looking at me, watching me.

I looked around the library and saw the students huddled together, sitting at tables surrounded by books, laptops, papers, and I saw it. I could see Avery sitting right there, books askew, papers piled, typing rapidly on her laptop, creating a paper that would wow every professor, laying the bricks of her bright future. This is her place. We found it.

I glanced at Scott. He was looking at the very place I was. He could see it too. He turned and winked at me. This connection, this family, was everything.

Scott called it the last true Fowler Family Vacation. I did not like saying that word *last*, but I had come to realize that I needed to accept things for what they were or I wouldn't be able to accept the little moments that came with them. There will be lots of lasts, and if I spent too much time cursing the word and being angry, I would lose the opportunity to make it last, make it count. This new positive epiphany gave me hope that I wasn't a lost cause.

Nobody told me that when you find this epiphany, when you recognize you're on the right path, you have to work to keep it, stay on it, because it's really easy to get lost again. Nobody told me I'd forget to pack that feeling when I went home.

***

Jason's apartment ended up being a perfect fit. The rent was even pretty reasonable. Jason's position was not super high-paying, so things would certainly be tight for a while, but it would mostly cover his expenses, and he was expected to move up the ladder rather quickly and he could use his savings to supplement for expenses in the meantime if needed. The apartment was in the East Village, an incredibly charming studio that was an 8-minute walk to Washington Square Park, and a short subway ride from his new office. We paid the deposit and the first and last month's rent. I insisted that as a graduation present he let us cover these costs, and he was certainly grateful. Originally for his graduation present, we had planned to offer to pay for a large chunk of his wedding expenses, so this felt right. I still had the funds saved for Columbia that were now not needed, so I was happy to help him out.

Jason rarely spoke of Hannah. I missed having her around, but he seemed to be moving on and I figured it would be best to follow his lead. *Let go.*

His move-in date was the 1st of July. Five weeks. 57 days. I watched him as he spoke with the landlord. He was so grown up all of a sudden. When did that happen? For a moment I could see the 3-year-old boy he used to be: Blonde hair, unusually deep voice for a child, very serious demeanor. He was Spiderman for his 3rd Halloween and then every day after for an entire year, at least. When did he stop wearing that Spiderman costume? By the time he was finished with that particular phase, the suit was up to his knees and elbows and tearing at the seams. Nobody told me that one day he'd be wearing it and the next day it would be at the bottom of his closet, and he'd never wear it again. I complained about that suit every day. I begged him to let me throw it out. Nobody told me I should have cherished those days. I should have appreciated his imagination; only he could see the web coming from his wrists, but it was there to him. I remembered his devastation when he left his Spiderman action figure, his best friend in the world, at the movie theater. Did I go back and get it? Did I buy him a new one? *Let him wear the damn costume. Buy a new one, a bigger one.* Maybe he'd still be wearing it. I chuckled at the image of this boy, this man, signing the lease on his first apartment while wearing a Spiderman costume. I should have let him be whoever he wanted, let him be Spiderman forever. I watched the man in front of me and realized he did just that. Not Spiderman, but he grew and he became a man and an amazing one at that. *Let go.*

We got a family picture in front of the Bethesda Fountain in Central Park. I knew I was going to have it put on the mantle at home. The Fowler Family, all smiling, all together. Maybe one of the last times. There's that word again. I looked at the smiling faces and I told myself, those are all genuine smiles. This was fun. We had fun. I didn't ruin anything. This time.

***

At dinner on our last evening in New York, I brought up the subject of furnishing Jason's apartment. It would be difficult and complicated for him to do this alone. Scott was planning to come out with Jason in July when he moved in to help, but actually buying and moving in furniture and supplies would have to come first, otherwise he'd have to extend his trip. We talked about online purchases, what we could ship, how much it would cost.

"I have an idea," I said suddenly, feeling quite proud of myself. I was personally enjoying my sudden optimism, and I hoped everyone else was as well. It felt like the Old Molly was back. I missed her. "Let's go shopping tomorrow, buy as much as we can for Jason's apartment and put it in a storage unit."

I looked over at Scott and continued, "Then on July 1st all you will have to do is get his stuff out of storage and move it into his apartment." I could tell by the look on everyone's faces that I had full Fowler support. "I'd like to use the rest of the money I saved on my commissions this spring to pay for it." Jason's face was tentative. I nodded at him and said, "I insist, Jason, let us give you a good start."

"One last Fowler Family Adventure," Scott announced. I tried not to let my smile fade with the mention of that word again. *Enjoy it. Make it count.*

I grabbed my phone and opened the travel app. "We're due to fly home tomorrow, so I'll change the flights and let the hotel know."

Avery and Jason were already looking on their phones at furniture and making lists of what they would buy and which stores to shop at. Jason got up from the table and came around to crouch down between our chairs.

"I just wanted to tell you both how much I appreciate everything you've done for me. I know this isn't what you imagined for me, New York, this job, moving so far from home, but I felt like I needed to start somewhere new, try something new." He put his hand over mine and looked at me directly and said, "Maybe it won't work, maybe it will, but this all feels right." I nodded. He was right, it did feel right. He also knew what that phrase meant to me.

"Fuck everyone else." We all said together. He gave us both a quick hug and a nod and headed back to Avery, telling her that she needed to get his approval before she made any decisions.

I excused myself outside to get the arrangements made for extending our stay. I could have done it at the table. I could have done it later. The truth was, I wanted to be alone for a minute. Optimistic Molly, the old Molly, was tired. She needed a break. My selfish, angry thoughts were pounding at the door to get out, and it was deafening. I needed a brief minute alone, to cry, kick something, curse the word *last*. Nobody told me that being alone was the last thing I should have wanted

to be.

Chapter 16 – The Mystery Neighbor

After New York I found myself very restless. Sitting alone with my thoughts was not an option. My smile had become real and my feelings had moved from bitterness and anger to nostalgia and pride, but if I sat alone too long, if I didn't stay busy, I slipped back. I grabbed my running shoes and hit the road. The first mile or so was always the worst. I questioned everything about myself starting with my sanity and ending with my judgment about whether or not I was actually a runner. Never, and I mean absolutely never, did I think about anything else. It's like the stress and the worries and the guilt just slipped away. I tried as many new routes as I could. I couldn't make it boring, I needed to keep it interesting, new. If I got bored, I started to think.

Today I happened to run down a road that had led to the Community Center. My kids attended preschool there. We had been a part of so many *Mommy and Me* classes there as well. Avery tried gymnastics there before she decided the leotard was *too itchy*. I stopped to look at the bulletin board. I don't know why but I wondered if they still had those preschool classes and if Ms. Beverly was still teaching them. She taught them both and they adored her. There were a lot of bulletins tacked to the corkboard, but not a single one of them mentioned the preschool. A young girl stepped outside and hung up another piece of paper.

"Excuse me," I asked, "Do they still teach preschool here?"

She shook her head. "Not in the last year or two, they couldn't afford to keep a teacher. The school districts are desperate for teachers and they can pay them a lot more than we can." She shrugged her shoulders. "It's too bad, I went to preschool here and I loved it. After Ms. Beverly retired they had to shut it down. They just couldn't fill the position." She turned to go back inside.

"Both of my kids went here too," I said in a solemn, quiet voice that was meant for no one.

"What year?" She said as she stopped midway through the door. "You look a little familiar."

"My son is just graduating college, so 18 years ago? And my daughter is 17, so 13 or so years ago or so." I absentmindedly glanced through the other notices, taking note of interesting class offerings.

"Are you Jason Fowler's mom?" She asked.

I turned to face her. "Yes…" I said tentatively.

"I'm Abby Goldman," She said, "Jason and I were friends. I moved away to New Hampshire, but Jason is the one kid I remember the most. I remember going to his house a few times and we -"

"- ate macaroni and cheese and corn dogs and watched *Dragon Tales*," I interrupted.

Her face lit up. "Yes!"

I leaned toward her, "Just a little secret between me and you, Jason didn't like that show or corn dogs, but he watched it and ate them because he liked you."

She blushed and looked away. "Tell him I said *hello* and to stop by if he'd like. I work Monday through Friday." I nodded. I didn't want to tell her he was moving. She disappeared through the door. Jason really did like Abby a lot. When she moved he cried for an hour. He was 4 years old, so he got over it quickly, but there was a period of about six months or so where he forgot she was gone and would ask if she could come over.

I debated whether I should tell him. It was highly unlikely that an old friend from 18 years ago would be enough to get him to change his mind, but what if it did? I shook my head to clear that selfish thought. I was still getting used to the new revelation of this fresh start, a new beginning, letting go. If I let him know Abby was back simply because I hoped it would change his mind, that was very underhanded and self-serving. On the other hand, if I didn't tell him, maybe I was messing with fate. Maybe they were soulmates. Maybe I should have just kept running.

***

Later that day I stepped out to get the mail. The kids were already receiving graduation cards in the mail. I wanted to throw them away, tear up those cards from well-wishers telling them how great it was that they're leaving their mother. It was not only the wrong thing to do, it didn't even feel right, but I also was an insensitive, selfish, petty bitch. Nevertheless, I didn't throw them out. I clenched my jaw and handed them over.

At the mailbox, I saw Mrs. Tumdale appear at the door of her house across the street. She was elderly and had lived there ever since we moved in 25 years ago. I had spoken to her maybe four times. In the last several years I had not seen her outside of her home much; I forgot she still lived there. She seemed to be struggling with her cane and the front steps. I rushed over to give her a hand. I quickly discarded the voice that told me that I wasn't being selfish by helping this woman. But I was; I was doing it to avoid the cards in the mailbox. The ones from friends and family I was actively adding to my list of backstabbers. Ones that were not only happy that my kids felt the need to run to the other side of the country, but they were also giving them money to help fund their escape.

"Oh goodness no, please, I can do this," She said as she tried to wave me off. I hovered next to her as she shuffled slowly to the mailbox. Her mailbox was full. It looked as if she hadn't checked her mail in months. Why was she doing it now? There's no way she could have carried all of this by herself with this cane. I pulled an armload out and told her I'd walk her in. It took exactly 23 minutes to take a round trip from the front door and back again. In her kitchen there were piles of frozen dinner boxes. The house smelled musty and old.

"I was just going to heat up my lunch dear, would you like one?" Her shaky hands pulled out another TV dinner from the freezer. One of at least 30.

"No, thank you," I said and started cleaning up her boxes and her kitchen.

"Please leave that," She said. I'll take care of it later. How are your kids, they must be getting so big."

Oh my. Here was someone who didn't know about my kids leaving. Someone who didn't say *you must be so proud*, or *I bet you're excited to have some alone time*. Someone I didn't have to add to my ever-growing list of double-crossers. I settled in to enjoy a conversation that didn't make me sad. A conversation that could have, would have happened months ago before everything went south. I realized as I sat there, watching her heat up her pathetic lunch, that although I yearned for a conversation that wasn't about the move, my kids, their plans, New York, my future, the empty nest, I didn't really have much else to talk about. My life was my kids. My kids were my life. I sat here at the kitchen table of a woman who was unaware of my situation. I reminded myself that this is what I wanted, just a moment to not talk about any of it, not hear how proud everyone was, not think about the future, but I found myself wanting to tell her rather than pretend it wasn't happening. Maybe I was more proud than bitter. Maybe I was improving.

She sat down to eat and I said, "Both of my kids just graduated, from high school and college. They're moving to New York."

She smiled at me. "I know, dear." She patted my hand gently. "I didn't mention it because I'm sure you're feeling a lot of things right now that sometimes you just don't want to talk about. You probably wish people would stop bringing it up, right?" She folded her napkin and laid down her fork. "You're proud, but you're sad. You're happy, but you're mad." I nodded quickly, shocked that someone was relating to me, shocked that it was this woman I had barely spoken to. She knew.

She chuckled, "I may be in my 80s now, but I remember feeling that way. My son went into the military, into the war. My other son went away to college that same summer. I lost them both." She took a small bite and set her fork down again. "People on the streets would stop me, ask about them, praise them. I yelled at people frequently, told them to mind their own business. They meant no harm. My Fred left me shortly after because I was so angry all the time. I wasn't the woman he married anymore. I thought I had nobody, but instead I pushed everyone away." She continued to eat as if she hadn't just dropped a nuclear truth bomb on me.

I felt all of the air leave my lungs. This was my story. She was me. I was her. She stood up from the table. "Go back to your beautiful family, Molly. Love them hard and then let them go." She pulled two cards out of her purse. "I kept meaning to walk these over to Avery and Jason, but it's a bit far. I'm glad you stopped by." I didn't even know she knew their names. I didn't know she knew my name. She shuffled into the other room and shouted, "GO HOME MOLLY." I chuckled and got up, at the last minute grabbing all the boxes off the counter and taking them with me.

***

When I got home both of the kids were at the kitchen table working on their laptops and eating a snack. Scott was napping in his chair. I kissed him lightly on his head and smoothed his hair. I made a silent promise to him to continue to be the wife he married, to love him hard and hold on tight. I told myself that even though I had become a liar, discovered maybe I always was, I planned on keeping that oath.

I handed the cards to the kids. They looked confused but opened them. They gasped, nearly in unison. She had put five $100 bills in them. In each card there was a photo of them. Avery must have been 5 and Jason was probably 11. I had never seen it before. They were sitting at a small table eating popsicles, both of their grins stained red and purple from their snack.

"Oh my god!" Avery laughed "I remember this day, do you?" She looked at Jason, whose eyes were dancing with fond remembrance.

"Of course!" He said softly. "We wanted to buy mom a birthday present and so we knocked on Mrs. Tumdale's door to see if we could earn money by doing chores for her. She gave us the most absurd chores to do, like push the chairs in at the dining room table, make sure all of the dandelions in the yard were picked. What else, Avery?"

She giggled. "We had to tell her cat a story."

Jason threw his head back in laughter. "We read *Cat in the Hat*. She gave us these popsicles and said we had to eat the entire popsicle in less than ten minutes."

Avery covered his face with her hands, laughing. "Oh, that's right! I took that so seriously. I didn't realize that ten minutes was a long time, so I devoured that thing and got my first brain freeze. I was afraid to say anything because I thought I did it wrong and she wouldn't pay us. I seriously thought I was dying." Avery stared at that picture thoughtfully. "I remember she paid us, but I don't remember how much, do you?"

He nodded. "She gave us each $20. I thought we were so rich. We argued for two days about what to buy for Mom until one day after school Mrs. Tumdale met us at the end of the driveway with a wrapped package and said that we left Mom's gift at her house." They both looked at me. "We were confused; we didn't remember there being a gift, we thought we were supposed to buy it with the money we earned, but we didn't question it. If she said we left it there, we must have. We gave it to you on your birthday."

Avery joined in. "Oh yea, it was the heart necklace with the J on one side and the A on the other." I reached up and touched my throat. I cherished that gift. I wore it every day. I still do.

I turned back toward her house, seeing it and her with renewed eyes. This was a mystery woman that I didn't know, a part of my children's lives I wasn't a part of. With tears in my eyes, I looked back at the kids and said, "Would you like me to put those in frames for you?"

"Yes." Jason looked at Avery. "But I also had another idea." Avery seemed to be on the same wavelength as Jason because she nodded and smiled. Maybe they have the *twin thing* too. They stood up and started for the front door. At the last minute, Avery turned around. "Let's go, Mom! Can you grab the popsicles from the freezer? Don't forget your phone, we need you to take the picture!" I smiled. I suddenly understood the plan.

***

Later that night I hung a picture frame on the wall of my office next to the index card. There were three photos in it, ones I will cherish forever. The first one was the one Mrs. Tumdale took years ago, two little kids with popsicle grins, who selflessly sought out a neighbor to earn money to buy their mother a present, who worked hard to finish every chore. Next was the second photo of my kids from earlier today. A re-creation of the first one. They looked the same, only now they were two big kids with popsicle grins who wanted to thank a neighbor for the kindness she showed them all those years ago. The third was a picture of Mrs. Tumdale. She was laughing as Jason and Avery retold the story of that day, her eyes sparkling. She also had a popsicle grin. She was unaware that I took the picture, but it captured her beautiful soul, her giving spirit. The kids had the same frame with the same pictures. It was a moment in time they will treasure. And so will I.

I looked back at that index card and thought about how I applied it to my life over the years. Probably too much. It was great advice, but it had a time and place. This card, the advice, was a disaster in the hands of a selfish mother, an excuse to act however they wanted. I found that I was selfish more often than I wanted. I took the frame down and put it in a drawer and walked out of my office. I wish I had done a lot of things differently in my life, both now and then. Guilt and regret were new feelings for me and I loathed them. I didn't like that version of myself. Sometimes I felt like I was moving forward, looking forward, getting better, focusing on the positive, eager for the next chapter. Then other times, I forget all of that.

Nobody told me that sometimes you really have to fuck up in order to wake up and that I was about to fuck up big time.

Chapter 17 – The Perception of Letting Go

The month of May was uneventful. For me anyway. I felt like I was becoming good at deceiving everyone around me. Maybe not in words, but in my conduct. I put on a happy face, pretended. Sometimes I felt like maybe it wasn't deception as much as playing a role. Maybe if I continued the charade it would become a genuine emotion.

I found myself with very little to do. The kids were busy studying for exams, finishing up final papers, and preparing for graduation events. My help and attention were not only not needed, not wanted. I was most certainly in the way, as I had been told in not so many words.

Miles took on the planning of the dual graduation party at the Salty Dog. He refused to even let me help. He said I had enough on my plate, but the truth was that I was quite hungry; my plate was bare. I tried not to act like I didn't have anything to do. I felt useless, so I kept busy. I saw Sophie a lot. We had begun to develop a genuine friendship. I thought about ditching her as soon as possible, but I found that she was actually an authentically kind person. I couldn't do that to her. It was fortunate for me that she did most of the talking, it gave me the opportunity to not bring my bitter, dark side to the table. We didn't speak much about the kids leaving. She never asked how I felt about it, which kind of was a relief. I figured because she wasn't a mother she wouldn't be able to understand anything I was feeling anyway. Not that anyone would. I saw other mothers handling this better than I was. Scott was managing this whole situation with his usual poise and composure. He was a rock; I was a swamp of despair.

I ran a lot. Every day I got stronger and faster. I felt the weight of my emotions fall off. I ran away from my thoughts. When I ran, time stood still, plans weren't being made, nobody talked about New York, nobody talked at all. The clock stopped. Sophie had asked to be "running buddies" but I wasn't up to that. I tried once, but I couldn't talk while I was panting and fighting for my life; I'm not sure she noticed though, because she had no problem carrying on a conversation by herself. She didn't even sweat. I'm pretty sure she could sing *Bohemian Rhapsody* while maintaining a steady 8 mph pace.

One day I ran all the way to *Beans By The Bay*, a coffee shop on the waterfront. Avery and I loved this place, it had a deck over the water and you could sit on their mismatched, funky furniture and drink the best coffee in town. As I jogged into the parking lot, I decided to go in and rest for a little while, get some water, catch my breath, and debate whether to call an Uber back home. I forgot it was five miles one way. That meant I'd have to run another five miles to get home. I wasn't prepared for that. I wanted to still use my legs this evening.

At the counter, I ordered water and a muffin. I wasn't hungry, but I felt guilty buying only water. I felt guilty about so many things lately. I heard a voice behind me say, "Mrs. Fowler?" I turned to find Hannah at a table with a book and a coffee on the table in front of her. I was surprised to hear her use my formal name. She had not called me *Mrs. Fowler* since the first day Jason brought her home. She was a young, shy 15-year-old girl with braces back then. She was a beautiful, confident woman now, but she looked apprehensive now as she sat there looking up at me. I had insisted from the beginning that she call me *Molly*, and she did; in the last few years, she started calling me *mom*, something I had cherished. It saddened me that we were already back to *Mrs. Fowler*. As if I needed another reason to feel down. I sat down at her table reluctantly, reminding myself silently that none of this was my business. Miles liked to tell me I smothered my kids, that I was too far into their business, but he was wrong. I did know my boundaries. I drew the line at personal relationships with boyfriends or girlfriends unless they asked for my advice or assistance. This is the reason why I knew so little of the reasons for their separation other than the fact that Jason wanted to move and she did not. He did not seem to have any need to open up to me further, and I was not going to probe him for answers, as much as I wanted to.

"How are you, Hannah? You can still call me Molly, by the way." I set my purchases on the table and squeezed her hand. I felt as unsure right now as she looked.

She smiled. "Sorry. How's Avery, she must be excited."

"You haven't talked to her?" I was surprised. They had been so close. Avery was nine when Jason and Hannah started dating. She adored Hannah. She grew up with her. They were sisters in all the ways that mattered. They were friends.

Hannah shook her head. "I haven't contacted her because Jason and I thought it best to have a clean break. All of it. Even Avery." Her smile, which had yet to reach her eyes, lowered even more with that admission. Neither of us spoke for a very long time. There were things I wanted to know, but there were also things I didn't want to know. I noted with only a hint of irony that Hannah was in the process of learning to let go as well. I could see that she had her own struggles and her own personal path to discover. That realization sparked silent kinship in me. She would be fine. Maybe I would be too.

"I wanted to tell you that I appreciate how kind you and your family were to me over the years, Mrs. Fo - Molly. You were like a second mom to me, and I'm sure you're worried about me, how I'm handling all of this, but I'll be okay. I promise." She didn't sound like she was confident in that. She fidgeted with her bookmark and appeared to be hesitant to speak further. "I loved Jason, love Jason, but we have grown to want different things in life." She stood up and gathered her stuff and gave me a small hesitant hug. Right before she went out the door I made a decision.

Do what feels right.

"Hannah!" I shouted as she turned around. "Can I have a ride home?"

***

After Hannah dropped me off, I showered. For the first time in a while I didn't cry in the shower. Maybe I was starting to let go. Maybe I was too tired. Maybe I ran out of tears. Nobody told me that could happen.

CHAPTER 18 - THE KITCHEN FLOOR DISPLAY

I opened my email and groaned. This client was relentless. After the disaster at that first showing, I passed them off on another agent. They had now gone through nearly every agent in the entire region and were dissatisfied with all of them. They were clearly high maintenance and that was the absolute last thing I needed, especially right now. I vowed to keep my word to Scott and the kids. While it would be nice to have something to do, I recently discovered that I didn't miss it. In fact, the more days that passed without the paperwork, the open houses, the client meetings, the happier I felt.

I went downstairs to plan dinner. Two days until Jason's graduation and three until Avery's. Make every day count. I had a special dinner planned tonight, a picnic at the waterfront park. We did that frequently in the summers when they were younger. Avery would play on the playground, usually with some new friend she just met; Jason and Scott would throw the ball around. Later Scott would walk with Avery along the waterfront, teaching her about tidepools and showing her how to find where the clams were in the sand, and turning over rocks to locate the crabs hiding beneath. I would sit with Jason during that time and we would talk about whatever he wanted to talk about. Sometimes it was professional wrestling, sometimes it was the latest Marvel movie. Since it was summertime, it was usually the Mariners and baseball, but occasionally the upcoming Seahawks season. Most of the time I just sat there and pretended to listen, wishing I could pull out my book and read. I wanted to go back and slap myself. *Just listen to him, Molly.* I should have taken a lesson from Scott. During those picnics, he was always present. He took time with each of them and I couldn't even sit through a conversation with my son about something that didn't interest me.

The sudden recognition of those self-centered thoughts I had, the precious time I wasted not listening to his own stories and thoughts, crushed me. How could I do that? Maybe I was recalling it inaccurately. Even if I was remembering it correctly, maybe the kids didn't even notice. Maybe I wasn't as good of a mom as I thought I was. Maybe that's why my kids are moving across the country.

I no longer felt up to going on a picnic. It wasn't going to be a special evening that brought back fond memories. I would only feel remorse for the lost moments. Worse yet, would I listen even now? I put the picnic foods and supplies back. I collapsed on the kitchen floor and cried. I was the only one home so I could let go, I could give in to the anger and the self-loathing. I wish I could say I felt better, but I didn't. I don't know how much time passed before I felt someone sit down on the floor next to me. I was startled and looked up suddenly, hoping it wasn't one Jason or Avery. Miles.

"Mols," He said sympathetically. I slumped into him. "I had a feeling I'd find you here. Well, not here on the floor, that's unexpected, but I kind of figured I'd be walking into a fiery disaster of some sort."

I chuckled, "The twin thing? It's been 30 years, Miles, maybe it's time to let the lie retire."

"No way, it's still funny." He stood up and grabbed my hand to pull me off the floor. We went to the deck and reminisced about the story behind the twin lie.

At the daycare we attended, there were twins just a little older than us. We convinced them that we also were twins and that we could read each other's minds. It drove them crazy thinking we were a more connected set of twins than they were. Somehow we managed to always keep up the act. One day when our father picked us up, he caught wind of our scheme and we worried the jig was up, but instead, he went along with it. It made it even more hilarious. We haven't obviously been to daycare in many years, but for the few years we did they tried everything they could to learn the trick to *The Twin Thing*. Truly the scam of the century. It felt good to laugh.

"Honestly, Milo, why are you really here?" I asked, suddenly serious again.

"I haven't seen your annoying face on my phone as much. I know this isn't easy for you, Mols, and you're just going to keep everything to yourself, that's who you are." He paused briefly and looked around the yard, trying to avoid eye contact. Deep conversations were not his favorite. "I assumed you would only let the crazy train out of the station when nobody was around, and clearly I was right." He turned his face and looked at me, his eyes full of something I haven't seen in a while - genuine concern. He continued, "I've seen you trying to be strong, but I know you're broken. You have to talk to someone, or that black hole of pain you have in there is going to just expand and take over and you'll be dealing with a real code red emergency situation, not just the one that's going on in your head." He sat quietly for a moment before adding, "You know what I'm talking about, Molly." I looked away. I hated it when he started talking about the past. Our deep childhood, sure, but there are dark things that we can't talk about, won't talk about. We buried it for a reason. But he knew me better than anyone because I was him, he was me. I was afraid he knew too much, who I really was, the selfish mother. I was probably a terrible sister too. I felt panicked.

"I'm fine, Miles, honestly." I stood up and started straightening up the deck, chairs, cushions, whatever I could find to stay busy.

"Yea, that kitchen floor display was a perfect example of fine." He stood up. "Look, you should probably speak to someone with a degree and a license, but I know you won't, and against my will I have earned a Ph.D. in *Molly Moods and Behaviors*, so talk to your brother at least." He began to walk to the front yard but turned suddenly and pointed. "Just remember, I'll charge you double if you cry, triple if I have to pick your old ass off the floor again."

I laughed as I followed him toward his truck, appreciative that we were back to the old Miles Humor. When he got to the truck he added, "I think it goes without saying, but I have a feeling I need to anyway: Talk to Scott. I know you well enough to know that you don't like to burden the people you love, and I know how much you love him. Let him take care of you for once." That one stuck hard in my gut. I looked down at the ground and blinked away the tears.

He started his truck and rolled down the window. "Seriously, though, come get a beer and spill your guts, and you can get a big serving of tough love from your twin, not this sappy bullshit. Pepper misses Aunt Molly, come visit her at least."

I scoffed, "She likes all visitors, even the UPS man."

"Well, unfortunately, you visit way more often than the UPS man," He yelled as he backed out of the driveway. "Quit being an asshole, Molly. Deal with your shit, I'm tired of being the smart sibling; that's your job."

I stood quietly thinking about this. "WAIT! Did you just say I was the smart sibling?"

"What??" He shouted out the window. "I can't hear you?" He pretended not to hear as his truck drove off down the road. A fleeting compliment, gone with the wind. I smiled. I'll take it.

***

I pulled myself together and packed the picnic basket again. We were still going, but I had a new idea, a new place. A new Fowler Adventure. Things were going to be different from now on, but that didn't mean that they had to be bad.

We took our picnic to Lake Harmony. It was a place we had never been to, but it was a beautiful area with well-kept lawns and picnic tables. They had a place to rent paddle boats and canoes. Scott rented two paddle boats and bought water guns from the general store. We raced, Scott and Avery versus Jason and Molly, drowning each other with lake water as soon as we got close enough. I could hear the laughter echoing out over the water.

After we returned the boats, we watched the sunset over the trees, the colors reflecting on the still lake. The four of us leaned against the car, absolutely drenched from the water fight. Scott pulled me into his side, kissed the top of my head. I took my eyes off the sunset long enough to look up at his face. He was staring out at the horizon, a small almost imperceptible smile on his face, the kind you can't help but have because the blissful feeling inside of you is overflowing. The colors of the sunset reflected in his green eyes. I remembered the night I met him, how I couldn't stop staring. I was doing it again.

I was interrupted by a spray of water to the face. Jason said, "Stop gawking at Dad, you're ruining the sunset." Scott picked up his water gun and defended my honor. When it got too dark to play, the ranger came over to let us know it was time to go. What happened next was something that we Fowlers still talk about, laugh about. *A Fowler Legend.*

When the ranger approached us he said, "Sorry folks, park's closing."

All at once the Fowlers, connected and bonded for life, said in unison "The moose out front shoulda told ya."

***

The twin thing doesn't really exist. What is real, however, is *The Fowler Thing*: Four people who share a common bond, years of memories, adventures, inside jokes, and movie quotes, especially *National Lampoon's Vacation*.

Nobody told me that even a heart that is broken, barely hanging on, can still hold so much love.

Nobody told me that the pieces of me that were broken, fragile, I did that. I broke my own heart, and I was the only one who could fix it. I was also the only one who could shatter what was left.

CHAPTER 19– THE CRAZY TRAIN DERAILS

I had become someone I didn't recognize. Some days, like the day at the lake, I was truly happy and was able to tell myself that all those negative thoughts about myself were preposterous. I made them up. I was a liar. I had this family and a big abundance of love around me. But it never truly went away. Something would happen, a small trigger, a reminder, and it was back to the New Version of Molly. The version that was likely going to live out her days alone, bitter, because nobody, not even me, liked her. Or at least they wouldn't when they found out who she had become. Anger and selfishness were apparently now part of my personality, which also made room for guilt and bitterness. They all walked in, took their shoes off and made themselves comfortable. Moved in.

I didn't cry at either graduation. I think maybe Scott was surprised I didn't show emotion because he brought me a pack of Kleenex to both ceremonies. I didn't cry because the ceremonies were bullshit. I just couldn't experience a companionship cry with women who were sobbing but would go on to see their kid every day for the next 4 years. They didn't earn the right to shed those tears. My kids were picking up those diplomas and walking away from me. I deserved to cry, but I didn't.

Not only was I still a selfish, angry mother, but I was also becoming petty. I had to put out more effort to hide the negative emotions and pretend the positive ones and it made me feel and act completely numb and neutral. Dead inside.

I thought I was hiding all of this pretty well, but my acting skills were rusty. At The Salty Dog grad party, Miles grabbed my arm and yanked me outside. He brought some serious tough love. He was done with the sappy bullshit. Done with the New Molly.

"You have only 16 days left with Jason and you can't even crack a real smile? You think he doesn't notice?" He was madder than I had ever seen him. "Get over yourself, Molly. Jason knows you're going to miss him, and he's going to miss you, but he needs his mom; the mom who has always given 100% of herself, not this shitty 5% you're bringing." He grabbed a rock and threw it into the water. "If you think showing Jason you're unhappy is going to change his mind, you're wrong, but it will make him feel like you're not supportive. Which mom do you want to be to your firstborn, a sad and angry Mom or a supportive and loving Mom?" He started to walk away, but turned back and added, "Oh, and Scott? I don't know how he is feeling, I haven't talked to him and I won't, but I can tell you haven't either. He is not going to stick around if this is who he's going to have to spend the rest of his life with." He did start walking away, but over his shoulder he said, "I warned you that this was going to happen if you didn't talk to someone, let out the pain. Now the crazy train is off the rails."

"Fuck you, Miles." I walked away too, further down the beach, into the darkness. "What the fuck do you know?" He doesn't know. He doesn't understand. The twin thing isn't real. He doesn't have any kids, how could he sit there and tell me what to think, how to feel, what to do. I sat on a log and cried. But he did know. He knew and I hated it.

"Mom?" Avery's voice was tentative and quiet. I jerked my head up, hoping she didn't hear or see what just happened. "Can I talk to you?" I nodded and motioned for her to sit next to me.

"I'm sorry, Mom. I didn't know this was going to make you so sad. I can back out if you want, go to UW. I shouldn't have done this." My heart clutched. My heart broke. I broke it.

"Avery, no. No, no, no, no." I hugged her tight and in that moment it all went away. I was a terrible person and an even worse mother. What have I done? What was I doing? I grabbed her face in my hands and said, "I am so incredibly proud of you. I am sad, yes, but I'm just sad that one era is ending. There's a new one coming and that one can and will be even better. I just have to figure this out for myself." She looked up at me, her big brown eyes still wet with tears. I continued. "You and Jason are going to go on and do amazing things, and we will have more Fowler Family Adventures, they'll just be different. We won't see the Wiggles in concert, but maybe Billy Joel."

"Or Taylor Swift?" She said happily, her face perking up for a moment.

"Absolutely not, " I said. She laughed. "That's an Uncle Miles Adventure," I added.

Her smile stayed as she nodded and said, "Thanks, Mom." She threw her arms around me and I held on as tightly as I could. "I'll go to Columbia," She said and rested her head on my shoulder, just as she did when she was two. I found that hearing her say those words didn't make my heart wrench this time, they did the opposite. The words I said to her were real, from the heart; I meant them. It was baffling how I could feel two different things at once, sad and happy, proud and bitter.

We walked back to the party hand in hand. She was telling me that Miles was planning on singing some Taylor Swift karaoke later. We laughed, taking bets on which song it would be. I looked up at Miles and thought *thank you*. He turned and looked at me and gave me a thumbs up. Sometimes I think this twin thing is real. He was so incredibly intuitive and knew exactly what to say. I couldn't even think the right things, let alone say them. Sadly, if we were twins I'd probably look like him, and that would be unfortunate. At that moment I swore he heard that thought, because he quickly turned around, looked at me, and flipped me off.

Nobody told me that everything was about to get so much worse, only I wasn't the victim, I was the antagonist.

Despite my protests, the Fowler household had begun a countdown. I would have preferred the ignorant method, but a big red number was displayed on the kitchen whiteboard every single day. I walked in that morning to see the number ten. Ten days until Jason flew to New York forever. Scott was going with him. Even with all of his apartment furnishings in storage, Jason couldn't move them alone, so it seemed logical for Scott to go with him. . Scott had asked me to buy their tickets quite some time ago. I did not. I could not. I refused. I was being stubborn, and I was aware of that. I avoided the topic as much as possible. It was absurd that even for a moment I thought that by not purchasing the tickets I could change any of this.

Starting tomorrow the whiteboard display would have a single digit. Soon it would be blank. Nothing left. Gone.

I sat in my office staring at my open laptop, the desktop showing a collage of pictures of the kids over the years. I took time to look at each image, recalling the memory behind them. They all had a story, a moment in time captured forever. I was trying to remind myself that we had lived an extraordinary life and I had no reason to regret a single moment. I was startled by Scott's voice at the door behind me.

"Are we leaving the 30th or early on the 1st?" I stared at him, unable to speak. I had never lied to Scott before and I couldn't start now. My silence gave him all the answers he needed. "Molly," He groaned. "Why haven't you bought the tickets? The price is just going to go up!" He kneeled down next to me. "If it's because you want to go, just buy two more tickets for you and Avery; we can all go, You just need to remember to bring your big muscles and patience." He reached over and squeezed my bicep, pretending to check my muscles, then dramatically grimaced. "Maybe just your patience." We both laughed.

The idea did make me feel better. A little. I tried to imagine what was worse, saying goodbye to my firstborn at Seatac airport and then driving home alone or leaving him in his apartment in New York and then flying home. Neither. I needed a different option. The truth was that I did want to see his apartment furnished. I wanted and needed to see him content with his decision. If I could see that he was ready to move on, that he was in a good place, maybe I would be too. A part of me thought maybe he wouldn't be happy and I could take him home with me. Take my baby back to his home and keep him there forever. Either of those outcomes would be fine with me.

I went to work. I bought four tickets to New York. When it came to booking the return flight, I hesitated. I only needed three tickets for the return flight. This did *NOT* feel right. The thought made me nauseous. I peeked behind me to make sure I was alone, then I bought four return tickets. I'd rather pay extra money to feed the illusion. I was a fool.

Nobody told me that sitting next to a vacant plane seat would destroy me; nobody told me there would be two of them.

∗∗∗

Scott and Jason went to a baseball game, so I planned an Avery Day. She loves books and especially old bookstores, so I mapped out every single one I could find within a day's drive and we planned to visit them all. In theory anyway, I forgot how long she could stare at books, so we weren't even halfway through the day and we were only on the third one. She met me at the check stand with six large books in her arms. She would add those to the nine others she bought at the other two stores.

"Really, Avery, what are you going to do with all of these books?" I scoffed.

"Duh, mom, read them." She rolled her eyes and plopped them on the counter.

I pulled my card from my purse and handed it to the clerk. "I mean when you -" I stopped before I finished that sentence. I still needed to get through Jason's move before I could even begin to process Avery's. Move-in day for Columbia was not until August 29th. I still had time.

She never answered the question I didn't finish, which was fine with me. I didn't want to talk about it anyway. We decided on a place to go for lunch. It was usually a big argument between us where we would eat, but she agreed on the first place I recommended. I stared at her and put my hand on her forehead. "Are you okay? Why aren't you arguing with me?"

She laughed and pulled away. "Yes, mom, I'm just hungry, now let's go." I noticed she had been quieter than normal in the car all morning. I let her pick the music, *The Mountain Goats, Pink Floyd, Taylor Swift, Bob Dylan*. I hoped the music, the bookstores, the books, the day as a whole, would cure whatever was bothering her. I trusted that if she needed to talk to me, she would, but I wouldn't press.

Whenever I go to a restaurant with my kids the first thing I do is scan the menu for what they would like to eat. It's a habit I can't break. It was, I suddenly reminded myself, a non-selfish thing to do. I looked after their needs first and not my own, and I still did. Maybe I wasn't that bad of a mother. As I'm scanning the list for Avery-approved things, I remembered the things she would and would not eat when she was a kid when we would eat out as a family. She was not a picky kid, but she only loved her mom's cooking, so she was hesitant to try anything that didn't come from her mama's hands. Plain spaghetti noodles or waffles were pretty much all she would eat for three years outside our home. Her taste had certainly changed over the years, but the memory made me smile. I caught sight of clams on the menu. I knew how much she loved them.

"Avery, they have clams, would you like those?"

"Maybe," She said absentmindedly. She seemed distracted. I'm not sure she was even reading the menu, she seemed to just be staring at it. I didn't want to upset her by asking what was wrong. If something was wrong she could say it. In my experience, asking if there is something wrong and there isn't, makes something suddenly wrong. She knew she could talk to me if there was, and if she was going to, this would be the perfect day.

She did order the clams, and she ate all of them. She seemed to brighten up a bit, I thought maybe she really was just hungry. After lunch, she suggested a walk on the boardwalk. We were in North Valley, a town we had been to several times when the kids were young. We almost bought a house here, North Valley has a great school district, but we settled on the home we've now raised our kids in. The town was close enough to drive to though, and we did frequently. She sat down on a bench.

"Can I talk to you, Mom?" I sensed this was coming. I put my *Mom Hat* on and prepared to solve the next puzzle, fix whatever was bothering her. "You know how I've been texting with my dorm roommate for a few weeks now? Caitlin?" I nodded. I had a feeling she'd want to meet her when we went to New York. Caitlin lives on the Upper East Side in a penthouse. I eased back and prepared to give her what she wanted. This was an easy problem. I can solve this with one simple word, *yes.* I relaxed.

"I'm supposed to move into Columbia on August 29th and we are moving Jason in on the 1st, and I know that's, like, a long time but -" She hesitated just a moment. My heart sank. This isn't the road we are supposed to be on. *Back it up Avery, back it up.* "- I was wondering if I could stay with Jason in New York for the summer, hang out with Caitlin, then Jason and Caitlin's parents can help move me in, you don't have to come out twice" She paused. I didn't speak because I had lost all feeling in my body. "I don't want to do this if it makes you sad, it seems like you've been less sad lately and I don't want to do anything that would make that happen again." I was still silent, unable to move, unable to speak. "Mom, please say something."

"Um…I…." Words came, but they weren't real words. Maybe I was having a stroke, my face was numb. I don't know how long it took, but I composed myself somehow. "You probably should ask Jason first," I laughed, trying to make light of it. "Maybe he doesn't want his kid sister around all summer."

"It was his idea." She said quietly. Betrayed by my own son. My face flushed. If I wasn't already having a stroke, I was going to. I had no words, nothing at all. "I asked Dad already, too," She added. "Dad said he was okay with it if you were." I sat there, still and quiet, trying to feel something. Anything. Scott should have said *no* first. How dare he leave this decision to me.

I tried to read her face, her eyes that were always so full of emotion. She was scared. I saw how badly she wanted this. How much she wanted me to say *yes*. I also saw that she would stay if I said *no*. I know why he left this decision to me. Those eyes. Those big brown eyes. Had he ever said no to them? No, he hadn't. I had to make this decision, break my daughter's heart or break my own. I heard my brother's voice in my head.

Let Go Molly

He's an idiot. But he's right. I nodded. "It's fine with me."

I've always loved giving my kids what they wanted; the joy on their face, the genuine happiness, even the ear-piercing shriek like the one I just got in my ear when she threw her arms around me. This hug. Ten fucking days and it's gone. How long before I forget what this feels like? How long before I am no longer the one making her squeal, putting that smile on her face. How long before I'm just the one she calls to complain about work or that her kids have been sick or acting up. How long did I have?

Ten Fucking Days. Nobody told me. Nobody.

***

I couldn't breathe. I tried to get back to the car, back home as soon as possible. It wasn't until I arrived at the car that I realized Avery was farther back. She already didn't want to be near me. We usually walked together. My heart ached.

I barely felt anything during the drive home. I was numb. I was broken. The buzzing in my head was deafening. These car rides used to be full of laughter and conversation. Did I listen? I thought of the picnics. *Just listen Molly.* Now we sat silent, the air thick with her disappointment. I thought I had more time to listen to her, but she had nothing more to say.

"Mom?" She asked quietly, her voice softer than I've ever heard. "I'm not going."

My body tensed. "Of course you are, Avery. Stop it. Why would you say that?" I was horrified to think that not only was she leaving me because she needed to get away from me, but that she was considering staying despite that. Despite me. In the history of the world, had there ever been a more despicable mother? Doubtful.

She looked at me, her eyes full of sadness. Regret. Guilt. I saw those emotions, because I knew those emotions. I felt them. I gave them to her.

"Because you're crying again," She said with a sound in her voice that resembled defeat. She turned her head back to face the front and spoke no more. I reached up and felt the tears that I didn't know were there. More guilt.

I said nothing. What could I say? I dug the hole and threw her down it. Words hung heavy between us. I glanced over to see her own eyes brimming with tears. I had so much guilt. What had I done?

CHAPTER 21 - THE CLEAN UP

I fucked up big time and I knew it, but I wasn't sure how to fix it. I told her *yes*, I gave her permission, I even begged her to go, but she announced to the whole family that she wasn't going. Then she stayed in her room for 29 hours. I knocked, pleaded, begged. I avoided Jason and Scott. They said nothing to me. I said nothing to them. What was there to say? The hardest part was that I didn't say *no*, but she felt it. She felt that I was still sad, still faking it, and she didn't want to hurt me. I wasn't sure what had changed. On the beach, she said the same thing and I convinced her it was okay to go and she agreed. It would have been easier if I had just actually done something wrong, actually said no, rather than just feel real emotions and have a daughter too perceptive to miss it.

Since nobody in the Fowler house was talking to me, I went to the one place I could get some real advice. I needed some tough love from my brother right now. I knew he was at the Dog so I pulled in and sat down at the bar. He put a beer in front of me.

"Why are you here? I figured you'd still be smothering the shit out of those poor kids." I told him about what happened, Avery's decision to go, and then to stay. How she hadn't left her room.

"Damn, Molly." He stood there silent. "I honestly don't know what to say. This is a tough one. I know I yelled at you, but you're doing the best you can. You have every right to feel a little depressed that they're leaving, nobody should be taking that away from you. Avery especially knows that, she's going through some big changes too." He sat down next to me. "I know how you raised them, to do whatever they wanted and reach for the stars, and that's what they did. I know you're happy and excited for them, but I also know you're unhappy and worried. You can be both.." He opened a beer of his own and took a swig. "Avery has to understand that it's okay to feel all of that at the same time. If you didn't, you'd be a shitty mother. Are you a shitty mother, Molly?"

I took a drink, contemplated that question I kept asking myself as well.. "Maybe I am, I don't know anymore."

He grabbed my empty bottle and went back behind the bar. "You're not. You know that."

I grabbed my purse. "This feels weird. I thought I was coming here for some tough love, did you hit your head this morning? You're pretty tall and these ceilings are low."

"I think maybe it's time to give Avery some of that tough love." He absentmindedly waved me off. "I'll be over in a bit after I finish up a few things."

***

Miles and Avery sat on the deck for 45 minutes. The three of us remained unmoving in the living room pretending to watch TV.

"I just don't understand what Miles could say to her that we couldn't say?" Scott wondered.

"I don't know, Scott," I said as I glanced towards the door. "But I'm willing to try anything. If she doesn't go, I'll never forgive myself. I let her down."

"Mom, no," Jason said. "Nobody expected you to be ecstatic that we're leaving. Nobody. We knew this would be hard for you, even Avery did. If I'm being completely honest, I think she's struggling just as much as you are. I think that's what all of this is about."

I looked up sharply. "What?" Did I hear that right? She was so thrilled about all of this, New York, Columbia; there's no way she was feeling sad or nervous at all. Or was she? Was I letting her down by not being perceptive enough about her feelings? That's what was different from the conversation at the beach. As we got closer to the date, and now with leaving early, maybe she got more and more anxious, sad even, uneasy. Maybe she used this as a reason to back out. Maybe she wanted me to say *no*. I couldn't let her give up on her dreams.

"She's not going to show it, and she'd definitely never admit it, but I see it." He smiled at me sadly. He's probably just saying all this to make me feel better, but it worked, so I appreciated it.

Just then the door opened. Avery's eyes were red from crying. "Avery has an announcement, everyone," Miles boomed. "She's decided to become a Taylor Swift groupie with me and we will follow her all over the world!" They both laughed. It was good to see her laugh. Miles raised his eyebrows at her and nodded seriously, "Offer still stands on that one if you change your mind, Aves."

She looked around the room and said, "I'm going to stay in New York this summer, and then go to Columbia." She met my eyes and smiled. "If that's okay with everyone." I nodded and we all stood up and went in for a group hug.

Miles wrapped his arms around all of us at once and said, "AHHH FOWLER HUG. How sweet!" He squeezed too tight and everyone squirmed to get out. "Let's go to the Dog and get some FOOD!" He shouted and headed for the door, waiting for the rest of us to follow.

***

Dinner was full of laughter, stories, jokes, teasing. Miles put some Taylor Swift karaoke on and he and Avery took turns, sometimes a duet. Even Jason got up once and sang with both of them. At one point Avery leaned close and laid her head on my shoulder. "I love you, Mom." I kissed the top of her head. There didn't have to be a time where I couldn't remember what this felt like. I was going to have to become a different kind of mother, that was for certain, but one thing that didn't have to change was that my kids would always know that my shoulder would be one they could rest their head on, my arms would always be open for a hug, and my home would always be ready for them. I looked at Scott and he smiled at me. A real smile. I hadn't seen one of those in a while. I wondered, maybe for the first time, if he felt all the things that I did as well, but hid them better. Maybe if he's going to be okay,

I'll be okay. Nobody told me that okay wasn't good enough.

Chapter 22 - The Important Moments

The time between graduation and July 1st was complicated. The kids no longer had school or work, Scott was using his vacation time, and I was sitting around waiting for the avalanche to take me away.

I oscillated between needing to spend every single minute with them to trying to be as far away as possible. The feeling was certainly mutual considering how much time they spent in their rooms with the doors shut. The feeling tore me up. I felt so much guilt about the times I sat in the bathroom just a few minutes longer than I needed, wanting some time to myself. How selfish was I? They were leaving in just over a week and I wanted to get away.

Any family, no matter how close you are, is not going to want to be together 24 hours a day for 10 days straight. Scott drove me crazy with his constant channel changing; just pick a show. When he wasn't wearing out the batteries on the remote he was out in his garage, pretending to be tinkering with something, staring out the window, or sweeping the already clean floor. I was not an example of someone who was handling anything well at all, so I wasn't going to say anything. Sweep the floor, stare out the window, I don't care; it was certainly more healthy than my coping mechanisms.

Jason, who has always been so calm and balanced, now seemed to be a little on edge, anxious, and irritable. Being in his presence was unpredictable. He could be quiet and silent or irrationally yelling about the empty almond milk carton.

Avery's anxiety and overthinking about the move and packing was becoming like a swarm of bees in the house: Annoying and everyone wanted it gone, but nobody wanted to touch it.

We were at day eight of the countdown. I woke up later than usual, and I was shocked to find nobody downstairs. Jason was an early riser, but the kitchen was empty with no sign of him. Normally by now, he'd be at the table, eating his scrambled eggs and fruit, drinking a protein shake, and catching up on his fitness YouTube channels. I stared at his seat, willing him to be there. I sat down alone at the table. If he was here now maybe I would watch one of his shows with him, let him explain to me what they were talking about, and I would listen.

I remembered back to a moment almost 20 years ago. He was 3 years old at the breakfast table, in that very seat, watching motorcycle racing and eating a peanut butter and jelly sandwich. At 3 years old it was difficult for him to understand why breakfast had to be a specified breakfast food item and not lunch. I had no answer to that question. Why did I have to feed him cereal or something with syrup on it? So if he wanted a peanut butter and jelly sandwich, he got one.

I wasn't surprised to find Avery still sleeping. Out of the four of us, she was our night owl. She claimed all of her best work was done in the middle of the night. I wasn't going to mess with perfection, so sleeping in was never something I had a problem with. Today, though, I desperately wanted to wake her and take her on one of the many adventures I had planned for us before she left. The list was long and our time was short. I decided to let her sleep. We had plenty of time. This was a lie I kept telling myself.

While my family slept, I ran. I still felt like I was just running away; either way, it was still one of the few things that didn't make me feel bad.

When I returned they were all awake. Scott was making breakfast sandwiches. They all made a big, dramatic show about how stinky I was after my run, so I made sure to give them all very big good morning hugs. Laughter, teasing, love. It was the soundtrack to our home.

After my shower, I stopped at the bottom of the stairs and watched them eat for a minute. I thought about all the times over the years that we did exactly this. Why didn't I try harder to enjoy the moment, live 100% for the people in front of me? Maybe I did. Maybe I didn't. I'll never really know, but I do know that those moments are important to me now. Watching my family sitting together, talking, and laughing gives me the feeling that those moments were special to them too, and that's all that matters.

CHAPTER 23 - THE PURPLE NOSE

The last full day before the move had arrived. The time leading up to it flew by because we were quite busy, we packed boxes and suitcases, we shopped for last-minute supplies and shipped them; we shopped for clothes and books that Avery didn't need but swore she did. I planned out all of the details of the events I had dreaded, fought against, and cursed for the last nine months. We played a lot. We went to baseball games, concerts. We visited friends and family. By the time that last full day came, we had nothing left to do. All of our suitcases were packed and sitting by the door. Anything that needed to be shipped was already brought to the post office and on its way. Any arrangements that were needed, the bank, mail forwarding, had been handled. Our flight left early the next day. Our alarms were set for 2:30 a.m. We found ourselves restless, all of us.

After breakfast, I found myself with so much extra food, french toast, bacon, scrambled eggs. It seemed a waste to throw it out. I looked out the window and saw Mrs. Tumdale's house and thought of her TV dinners.

I rang her doorbell and waited. She took some time to get to the door. When she answered I noted how much bigger her smile had become since that day we came over with popsicles. The picture frame I gave her was hanging prominently on her wall.

I watched her devour the breakfast. There were more TV dinner boxes on the counter. She shouldn't have to eat that garbage when I had so much extra food, and I was about to have so much more. I knew she would not accept anything that resembled charity, but watching how much she enjoyed the breakfast made me feel like I had to do something. I sent a text to Sophie. I had an idea; an idea that could help my new friend realize a lifelong dream and give an elderly woman something to look forward to every day.

***

I sat on the back deck with a book I hadn't opened yet, my thoughts currently not dark, angry, or bitter. I felt content. I felt happy. I felt hopeful. I had spoken to Sophie about an idea I had for Mrs. Tumdale, and possibly others. She was beyond excited. She talked so fast it made my head spin.

I thought about Jason starting his new job next week. I wasn't feeling sad or like I was being abandoned; I was excited for him, I was proud.

Avery was going to have an amazing summer adventure with her friend, as well as her brother. I was nervous about this, but I let go, she would be fine. She was a more mature and capable woman than most people twice her age. Soon her plans would all start falling into place. She was going to her dream school, and then she'd take on the world. I found it funny how quickly I could go from feeling fine to awful, laughing at myself to berating myself. I was a merry-go-round full of loony birds.

I watched Scott mowing the lawn. I thought about what Mrs. Tumdale said about Fred leaving her because she was no longer the woman he married. I couldn't imagine that happening to us. I felt like the months leading up to this day were difficult, I was difficult, but if Scott can stand by me through that, he wasn't going anywhere and neither was I. I wasn't sure how it would feel after we came back from New York alone, the empty house, the silence, but I felt we could navigate it together.

Avery plopped down in the lounge chair next to me and picked up my book, but then rapidly tossed it aside. "Ugh. Why do you read this trash?" She didn't like my choice of reading material. They weren't classics. They weren't philosophical. They weren't in French. I rolled my eyes and picked up her book. *The Alchemist.*

"Again?" I asked, not at all surprised. She read this book at least 100 times.

"I'm actually thinking of translating it into Latin," She said, beaming.

"You don't speak Latin, Avery," I pointed out, quickly realizing my mistake.

"Not yet, but I can teach myself." She taught herself a lot of things. She actually is the one who taught herself to speak French. "So, Mom," She asked as she put a pair of large, funky, purple sunglasses on. "What are you going to do while we're gone?"

I found the question amusing. It sounded like she was asking what I was going to do for the afternoon while they were at the movies, rather than moving across the country. I couldn't help but smile. "The same things as usual, why would I do anything differently?"

She rolled her eyes and threw her head back. "You need a hobby, Mom, other than sitting on the back deck fantasizing about dad while he works in the yard, which is disgusting by the way, please stop." She pretended to gag.

"I'm not doing that, Avery, I was just out here reading." I slapped her arm with my book, but she was right, I was.

"No, you weren't!" She laughed, trying to dodge my arm slap. "You haven't even opened it, you've been staring at Dad, I watched you from the kitchen while I was eating. Ten minutes, mom. Ew. I almost lost my appetite." She grinned at me. She loved teasing me. I was going to miss this. She was going to miss this. This didn't have to change.

"Let's find a less revolting subject now, shall we?" She pulled out a notebook and a pen from thin air. "Let's talk about hobbies." She always seemed to have those hidden somewhere, always ready to take notes. She positioned her pen and said, "You don't have any, so let's talk about ones you might like to try."

"I have hobbies, lots of them." I tried to come up with some. "I read! I like music!"

"Not a hobby, and also not a hobby." To make a point she wrote them both down and crossed them off. She looked again at me expectantly. "What else can I write down and cross off?" She wrote *cooking a*nd then crossed it off. You cook for your family, it's not a hobby. How did she know I was going to say that? I decided to not mention my conversation with Sophie; I was sure she'd cross that idea off as well. *Not a hobby.* It was a business venture.

She wrote down the word *hiking*. "Maybe Uncle Miles can teach you about hiking? He and Pepper go all the time. That might be an interesting hobby for you." She contemplated that.

I snorted. "Avery, hiking is just taking a walk in the woods, how hard can it be? I don't need to be taught how to walk in the woods by my brother."

She laughed and said, "I'm telling him you said that." She crossed out *hiking* and wrote *down afraid of bears*.

"I run!" I remembered suddenly, super proud of myself for thinking of something. She wrote it down.

"Yes, that is true. You do run. Let's talk about that. Running is exercise, not technically a hobby, although I feel like you don't do it for either of those reasons. So, let's expand it. Why don't you train to run a race again? Remember when you did the Rock and Roll Half Marathon? You trained really hard, you were so focused, you had charts and goals, we were all so proud of you! Not just when we were standing at the finish line cheering you on, but the whole process was so amazing to watch. I was in awe of you."

I was speechless. I did love that. The training, the race, the finish line. Other than my kids, it was one of my proudest accomplishments. I hadn't even considered the fact that other people may have admired what I had done. I considered this for a moment. It wouldn't be that much work, I was already putting in lots of time and miles. I'd just have to put together some daily and weekly goals. I could put them on a spreadsheet. That thought made me smile.

"Oh, mom, you're thinking of spreadsheets again, aren't you?" We both laughed. It was an ongoing joke about how much I loved spreadsheets. They bought me a coffee mug for Christmas that says "This calls for a spreadsheet!" I had just used it that morning.

"Yes, I'll do it." I said to Avery. "I'll train for a race. A marathon." I blurted out. I knew I may be in over my head, but after hearing Avery's confidence and pride in me, I felt I could run around the world.

She beamed. "I was hoping you'd say that! The Boston Marathon is in October. You could fly out, we could all go to Boston and cheer you on. I know it's only 3 months away, but you totally could do it."

I felt like I could do anything at that moment. I reached my hand out and she shook it, making a pact. "It's a deal, I'll do it."

She jumped up and yelled across the yard. "Dad! Mom's going to run a marathon!"

He looked confused. He looked at his watch dramatically and then back at us. "Okay, but will you make it back in time for dinner?" Avery threw her head back in laughter. She loved her dad's stupid humor. I loved her laugh. I loved seeing her happy. I worried that college would break her, change her. I worried she'd struggle and tell nobody. I worried that she would cry alone. I worried that I wouldn't be there when she needed me. I worried that this loud, infectious laugh would become a chuckle, and then it would disappear. Nobody told me that this was not the child I should be worried about.

***

After the sun went down the four of us hung around the living room. We all knew we had to go to bed, that the 2:30 a.m. alarm clock was going to come very quickly. Avery spoke up first. "So, I was wondering if anyone wanted to play Clown Bingo?" I watched Jason smile. Scott couldn't help but grin as well. We played that game when the kids were little. All the time. Every Friday night, many rounds of Clown Bingo, popcorn, candy, and laughter. We hadn't played it in maybe 8 years. One last time. All of our smiles said everything.

"I'll go get it!" She announced.

"I'll make popcorn." Jason got up and went to the kitchen.

I looked at Scott. We both knew what was next. He grabbed his keys, kissed me on the cheek and whispered, "I'll be right back, I'll go get some candy. Don't let her take the purple nose card."

I'm not sure if I had ever loved him more than that moment. That alarm was going to hurt, 2:30 was going to come so quickly, but this was exactly what I needed. Exactly what we all needed. Avery passed out the pieces with a grin on her face. She kept the purple nose card and I didn't stop her, neither would Scott. As she set it on her seat she smiled at it, remembering the inside joke, the many moments that surrounded the card that she and her father shared.

Nobody told me that sometimes it's okay to break the rules, stay up late, eat candy, dance in the rain, jump in the puddles, run on the stairs, eat peanut butter and jelly sandwich for breakfast. These are the things they remember.

CHAPTER 24- THE FIRST DAY OF JULY

Our second time in New York was fast, structured, and uneventful. We moved Jason in, set up his apartment, and left. There wasn't any time for sightseeing. There wasn't any time for emotional scenes or crying. I made a vow to myself that I wouldn't cry. I thought of having some real heart-to-heart mom talks with them, giving them advice, telling them they could come home at any time, but I decided against it. They knew everything I would say already. We all felt like this move and this trip was a good thing and we were happy, so we just did what needed to be done and left. I didn't need to *Mom it up*, as the kids liked to say. That was my intention anyway.

On our last night there we ate take-out in Jason's apartment. When we left, the hugs and goodbyes were not emotional, just *see you later, have a nice flight, call me or text me anytime, I love you*. Scott and I were silent on the way to the hotel in the cab. He reached over and squeezed my hand and I smiled at him. Just the two of us, I thought. I wondered what he was thinking, but I didn't ask. I probably should have.

I was brushing my teeth and Scott was flipping through the channels when a knock came on our hotel door. We looked at each other puzzled. At the door stood our kids, dressed in their pajamas, smiling. "What the - " I said, confused, but not upset to see them.

Avery pulled the Clown Bingo game out from behind her. "One more round?"

Jason asked, "Then maybe we could stay the night, see you off in the morning?" He pulled something out from behind his back. Popcorn.

"One last Fowler Family Adventure," Avery piped in grinning. "A slumber party!" I was speechless again. They continuously surprised me. I pulled them in for a hug. I didn't let go. They didn't let go.

From behind me Scott yelled, "I get the card with the purple nose this time!" Avery laughed. I remembered back to a time, Avery in her Barbie nightgown, waiting anxiously for that piece to be called. When the purple circle was drawn, the caller would announce *Purple nose! Does anyone have a purple nose?* She would giggle and say *I've got a purple nose!* Then she would look to her father, who would lean in and inspect her nose and say *Nope, your nose isn't purple.* And they would laugh. Every time. Then on the off chance Avery let him have the card, they would do it all over again, and she would inspect his nose. They could have done this little scene with any of the colors, but it was always the purple nose for some reason. It was special. It was theirs.

Scott got out of bed and walked up behind us and joined the squeeze. "I'm going to get all the candy from the vending machine," He whispered. "I need extra arms, Avery, come with me."

They started off down the hall. Father and daughter, discussing candy and purple noses, laughing, his arm slung around her shoulders.

I let Jason in and we put the popcorn in the microwave. We sat down together. He was quiet.

"You okay?" I asked. He nodded.

"Sometimes I miss Hannah. I wish she would change her mind and come to New York." I nodded, understanding. They were together for a really long time. She was his best friend.

"Have you talked to her?" I asked. He shook his head. We spoke for a few more minutes before the others came back. He said they had agreed to a clean break, and so neither of them had reached out to the other. I told him finally about running into Abby. He smiled faintly. "I totally forgot about her." I apologized for not telling him sooner. He said it was fine, he probably wouldn't have gone to see her anyway. At least I could put that guilt away.

I put my arm around him. "I'm sorry about Hannah, Jay. I know you love her. I think you should try to reach out to her, even just a text to say hi, try to keep in touch. Six years is a really long time to be with someone every day and then not see them anymore."

He nodded. He looked at me and his eyes were glassy as if he might cry. "So is 22 years," He said softly. Oh, God. My heart stopped. I pulled him in for a tight hug. I worried so much about Avery leaving, about missing her, about her missing me. My boy, my firstborn, the one who made me a mom and taught me how to be one, was always so strong that I had neglected to consider that he might be scared, worried, unsure of the future; that leaving his mom, his dad, his home, Hannah, was so much scarier than he thought now that he was facing it. "I'll always be there Jason, always. Remember that." I put his face in my hands. "Do you remember that song we used to sing together when you were little before Avery was born and it was just us?" I pulled out my phone and showed him that my contact on my phone for him said Jason, but it had a sunshine emoji with it. He smiled. He grabbed my phone and called his phone from it. The ringtone started playing *You Are My Sunshine*. I gasped.

He said, "I never have my ringer on, but I do have it on for you because I like to hear this before I talk to you."

I could hear them fumbling with the lock, so I knew this special moment was over, but it was one I'd never forget. This boy was not my emotional one. He was serious and matter-of-fact, always had been; but for one moment in time, the last real moment we would share alone before we left, he let his guard down and let me in. Nobody told me that there was so much he wasn't saying.

Chapter 25 - The Middle

A Note From The Real "Molly"

I know that this part of the book usually comes at the end or the beginning, but I felt it appropriate to place it here, in the middle, between the Before and the After.

Molly is me, her thoughts, fears, feelings. I was raw and honest and vulnerable. It was terrifying. The story for dramatic purposes brings Molly's experience to a more extreme level than mine at times. The horses on my delusion wagon went straight for the river, too, but mine made it across, hers rode the rapids for a while. Maybe I'm just saying that so you don't think I'm a terrible person (I told you I'm Molly!)

The basis of the Fowler family is mine, but very extreme and exaggerated at times, at their request and for confidentiality. Almost all of the memories Molly has of their childhood are real; they're stories from our life, maybe just a little dramatized.

During my research for the book, I spoke to women who had been through the empty nest. I found a lot of them dealt with similar situations, but I sensed a lot of holding back. I know I would have too.

During the writing process, I shared some of my early drafts with those women, as well as a few others, looking for feedback on whether I was on the right path, telling the right story, and whether Molly was likable. I was terrified, I exposed myself. That's when I started to get the truth, the harsh reality, the real conversations; the admission that they felt, did, and said the same things, that they thought they were alone. They suddenly felt seen, understood.

Some women did not feel this way, they felt the empty nest was easy, they welcomed it, cherished the time with their husband, and grew together. Those women are liars; however, I understand their need to maintain the illusion, spin the fantasy. Also, I respect the need for privacy.

The second half only touches a little bit on the parenting part of the empty nest. It's a really big deal for sure, how your role as a mother changes and the patience it requires, letting your suddenly adult child lead the way on what they require from you without overstepping or neglecting. At one point or another, you'll do both of those things. They'll forgive you, and you'll forgive yourself, and you'll learn.

The second half hones in on how you change as a woman, redefining who you are, what is expected of you, what you expect of yourself.

The biggest part of the second half, however, focuses on the changes in the marriage. This is where the experiences are all over the map, and not at all limited to empty nesters. All of them, every one of them, used the word communication in their advice on how to survive it, what they should have done differently. It sounded easy enough to me, and also quite obvious.

The problem with communication is that it's deceptive. You can only hear what is being said, and what isn't said is usually what lights the fuse on the bomb.

Nobody told me.

CHAPTER 26 - THE RETURN OF THE LIAR

For 259 days I was a mess, on the inside and sometimes on the outside. I cursed and feared the day my kids would move to New York. The day came and went and I survived. It wasn't so bad.

I dreaded sitting next to those two empty seats on the plane. I was afraid of seeing Scott's face when he realized what I had done. He wasn't mad at all, and he didn't have a look of pity and disappointment on his face. Those two empty seats didn't upset me, and when the flight attendant filled them with standby passengers, I didn't scream at her, I didn't sob uncontrollably. Scott didn't have to give me a sedative and make excuses for me after I fell asleep.

I forgot to shut the kids' bedroom doors before I left, which was not a problem at all. Seeing Jason's room, barren of everything except the large furniture didn't tear my insides apart and I did not weep into his pillow for an hour. Avery's room looked as if she had just left for school, bed unmade, makeup on the dresser, book open on the desk. That didn't at all make me feel at all useless, like her childhood, the things I'd given her, the life she'd lived didn't matter anymore, she didn't need them. Didn't need me. I was fine.

The empty nest was not that bad.

None of these things are true.

CHAPTER 27 - THE EMPTY HOUSE

The empty house was dismal. Nobody told me how depressing a silent house could be. I allowed myself some time to wallow in self-pity, but it wasn't long before I found myself no longer hurting. The kids communicated regularly, calling and texting both of us every day, sometimes multiple times a day. I let them take the lead on this part. I knew when to text a quick check-in, and what to say that wasn't too intrusive or nosy. I stared at my phone, anxiously awaiting the next text, another call, details of the lives they were living without me. After every phone call or FaceTime, I would find myself unable to stop smiling. They were thriving. I could see that they were genuinely happy.

As the days passed I found the ache felt progressively fade. I thought I wanted and deserved to feel the misery, but I found myself unexpectedly beginning to feel like myself again, the *Old Molly*. I felt like I was navigating this part very well. I would have loved to call and text them all day long; however, it was a conversation with Sophie that pointed me in this direction, letting them take the reins in communication, both in amount and content, especially in the early days. Sophie's mother had not been the mother she needed when she moved out, still wasn't, and she rarely spoke to her. It made me look a little closer at how I would and should engage with them during this transition.

I had developed a few habits that kept me sane. The first was that my phone was never off and the ringer was always on the highest volume. This probably seemed completely acceptable and normal to most mothers whose children live across the country, I'm sure, but Scott was not impressed with full volume notifications from *Candy Crush* at 2:00 a.m. The second was the fully stocked duffle bag in my trunk. I was ready to go at the first distress call. I called it being prepared, Scott called it paranoid. The third was memorizing the daily outgoing flights from Seatac. At any given moment I could tell you which flight I would be on if I needed to. I even knew the traffic patterns well enough to know what time of the day I'd need to give more time and the alternate routes to take if I had to. This all may or may not have been toxic, but I figured it wasn't hurting anyone. Only it was. The only thing that mattered was that I wasn't hurting. That's because I was selfish.

***

Miles joined us for dinner one night and of course, asked how the kids were settling in. Scott and I took turns telling him stories and adventures they shared with us. He said, "How many times a day do you call them?"

I said, "None." He stayed silent and looked to Scott for confirmation.

"It's true," Scott added and winked at me.

"You never call your kids, Molly? Never?"

"I let them call me first. I'll text them just to say hi if it's been a while and would like to check-in, but I leave the timing and amount of communication up to them." I continued to eat, ignoring the pit in my stomach and the voice in the back of my head that tried to tell me I was being a terrible mother for ignoring them, that they probably felt isolated and abandoned by their mother.

Miles dropped his fork and stood up. He started clapping. "I'm impressed. You're holding up better than I expected. I thought we'd be peeling you off the ceiling by now."

Scott reached over and rubbed my hand. "It's been tough, but we're getting through. We're both looking forward to seeing them next month when we move Avery into Columbia." I gritted my teeth at those words. Tough? What did he know? He's been fine. He's been going about his day as if nothing had changed. For two days I did not get out of bed and he didn't even notice. I smiled at him and tried not to pull my hand away. I expected an Oscar for this performance. I had both of these men fooled. The whole world, really.

***

I started more actively training for the marathon. It felt good to have a goal and it felt even better to have something to occupy my mind.

I created a spreadsheet laying out the training schedule all the way up until the day of the race. Even after missing some time while we moved Jason into his apartment, I was still ahead of schedule. The remaining time was spent doing workouts such as cross-training, yoga, strength training, and pilates. I had signed up for a gym that had all of these classes, as well as a pool. I was currently enrolled in a once-a-week yoga class and a spin class, as well as twice a week I was doing strength training with a personal trainer, and I had a lane booked 3 mornings a week for swimming. I was currently running a steady full half-marathon distance on Wednesdays, 7 miles on Mondays and Fridays, and 4 miles on Sundays, which was the day I would increase my pace just slightly. I felt stronger every day, both mentally and physically.

I truly felt like my life was back on track. I was staying busy, which was keeping me out of the quiet, empty house, which I felt was the key to my healing process.

The only problem was that my house wasn't empty, the man I spent my whole life with, raised my children with, was still there and that he was becoming more and more lonely by the day. Nobody told me that I was pushing away the one person I should have been leaning on.

Chapter 28 - The Partners

A few weeks prior Mrs. Tumdale had inspired a business idea that I passed along to Sophie. She had been over the moon with excitement about it. I remembered that when discussing her frustration with her current job as a social worker, she confided her lifelong dream of becoming a chef. When I told her about Mrs. Tumdale and the frozen meals I lit a fire under her. We discussed putting something into place that would make and deliver meals to the elderly, disabled, and those unable to get around very well. It would also provide meal prep kits for busy mothers, working mothers and fathers, single parents, etc. Obviously, there were restaurants that delivered pre-cooked meals, and many online companies were already established in the meal prep industry, but how many were small, hometown businesses that personally delivered? Did they have a drive-thru for fast pick-up after work?

She called me and texted me daily regarding this. Originally when I spoke to her about it, I thought it may be something *she* would want to pursue, but I didn't necessarily mean that I was going to as well. I had a job already, as well as a family. Well, I did anyway.

One Saturday morning I saw her running in the park and ran the other way. I felt so much guilt about that. She was such a wonderful person and had become a really great friend, I shouldn't be running from her. Literally.

It was a Sunday morning at the beginning of July, just about a week after we returned from New York. I was on the home stretch, finishing up a quick 5K, having definitely beaten my last time. I could feel my phone vibrating in my pack. I always answered the phone when one of the kids called, even if I was in the middle of a run, so I pulled it out to check. *Sophie*. I put it back in and kept running. It started again. *Sophie*. I stopped and stared at the red and green buttons, and Sophie's smiling face that she insisted I put as her contact photo. *Accept* or *Decline*? I thought about Avery and Jason and if there was ever a time that they needed someone and that person didn't answer their phone just because they didn't feel like it. Maybe Sophie needed me. Maybe she was just bored. Either way, I pressed *green*.

I prepared myself for her chipper voice and excessively positive attitude.

She was crying. "Molly, I need your help, I don't know what to do." *Mom mode reactivated.* Someone needed me. It didn't matter what it was or who it was; I was needed. Before I could understand a solid coherent sentence through her sobbing, I turned onto my street and my heart stopped. I saw Sophie's car in front of my house. No, not my house, I realized - Mrs. Tumdale's house. I ended the call and sprinted down the street.

She had been knocking on Mrs. Tumdale's door for the better part of 30 minutes with no response. This wasn't normal. She did take a while to get to the door, but never this long. Tears were streaming down Sophie's face. I realized suddenly that Sophie seemed awfully attached to someone she had not even been introduced to yet. *Maybe you should answer your phone more often, Molly.* I was so selfish.

"I'm so scared, Molly." She whimpered and started slamming her body into the door as if she were out Hulk and she could break through it with her tiny, elf-like frame. She was going to hurt herself.

While she was attempting to dislocate her shoulder, I found a key under the mat. "Soph, stop it, I found a key."

She stopped and said, "Oh, I didn't think to look there."

We entered the house, Sophie running ahead of me. "Oh my God!" She yelled, "Call an ambulance!"

Mrs. Tumdale had fallen. She broke her hip and her collarbone. She had been there for 36 hours. I should have checked on her. More guilt. So much more.

After the ambulance left, I sat down next to Sophie on the faded green couch. She was always so full of energy, but she now sat motionless, her face showing clear distress and worry. "You never told me that you knew Mrs. Tumdale," I said.

She stayed silent for a short time before she said in a soft voice, "I don't." She closed her eyes, tears still in the corners of her eyes. "At least, I didn't." She took the tissue I offered her and wiped her eyes. "Do you remember before you left when you told me about her, about your business idea?" She looked at me, her eyes suddenly lit with the fire I previously put there, a welcome change from the sadness.

I nodded, encouraging her to continue. "I loved your suggestion, still love it. I can't stop thinking about it." She stood and started pacing the room as if just speaking of it gave her too much energy to contain. "While you were gone I stopped by and introduced myself. I instantly felt an attachment to her." She picked at a loose thread on her coat. "She reminded me of my grandmother. I started stopping by often, bringing her dinners as we discussed previously, but also helping her by straightening up the house and mild cleaning." I looked around the room and just now noticed that the house didn't smell as musty and old and it was much neater than the last time I was here.

Sophie sat back down next to me and put her hand over mine and continued, "I know you have a lot on your plate and how busy you are, but I'm really excited about this business venture, and now that I know Mrs. Tumdale and also after what happened today, I am going to do this with or without you."

"Oh my God," I groaned. All those calls I've been dodging from her. "I'm so sorry, Sophie."

She shook her head. "No, I'm the one who's sorry. You don't have time for this. I shouldn't have been bothering you. Your kids just moved away, you already have a full-time job, and you're working so hard to train for the marathon." She grasped my hand. "You lit a fire in me, but you have no obligation to be a part of any of it." She wiped her eyes and blew her nose and then let out a quick laugh. "I told you I was a terrible social worker." I tried not to, but I couldn't help but laugh with her.

I considered all of this. I didn't want to sell houses anymore anyway. My kids were gone. Why not?

I suddenly got serious and looked at her and said, "Then quit. Partners?" I stuck my hand out in her direction. She smiled and reached her hand out to grasp mine, her face glowing with excitement. This would be a fresh start for Sophie, a new beginning. And me as well. We shook hands, an agreement amongst friends, partners.

***

I rode with Sophie to the hospital. The car ride became a brainstorming session, I took notes on the back of a take-out menu. I couldn't wait to tell Mrs. Tumdale about this.

Mrs. Tumdale clapped her hands after we finished. "Oh yes, Sophie mentioned the idea. I'm pleased you're moving forward because I have something for you both. Now, keep in mind that I can probably only work a few days a week, but I don't expect any compensation, maybe just a ride." She motioned towards a chair across the room. "Molly, there's an envelope in my purse, can you grab it?"

I went to her purse and pulled out a white envelope. It had our names written in shaky handwriting on the front. I looked at Sophie and then at Mrs. Tumdale. She gestured for me to open it. I removed a check in my name in the amount of $50,000.

Sophie threw her hand over her mouth. "Oh my God," She whispered through her fingers.

I laid the check on her bed. "We can't take this."

She pushed it back toward me. "I don't need to be listed as a formal partner, but I would like to invest in your business. I believe in you both and this is something the community needs." She looked at me, tears in her eyes. "You saved my life, Molly, and I'm not just talking about today. You came to visit a lonely old lady, brought popsicles, your children, and continued to allow me to be a part of your family. And those TV dinners really *are* awful!"

Sophie and I laughed and glanced at each other. We hadn't considered a third partner, but it felt right. Considering the glow on her face, she was feeling pretty good about the decision as well.

We accepted her offer. "I have one stipulation!" I announced, glancing at Sophie for a quick unspoken approval. "You'll be an official partner."

She smiled. "I also have a condition." She got serious, folded her hands, and looked down. "You need to start calling me Jane."

***

As Sophie and I were walking through the parking lot back to her car, I pulled her in for a hug. She was surprised. "Oh, I didn't take you for a hugger," She said.

"I'm not," I said. "But I'm a mom, and I know when someone needs a hug. Even when that person is me."

She smiled. We were friends, real friends. Friends who were going to go on and start a business, a partnership.

Nobody told me that the journey of self-discovery isn't a direct path, from one place to the next; it's a winding road, with many stops along the way.

CHAPTER 29 - THE MERMAID TANK

Since partnering with Sophie and Jane, I had not officially put my notice in at the agency, but I also had not taken on any new clients. One of our newer agents was a young, single mother who frequently had to drop clients suddenly or postpone or even cancel showings when a matter arose with one of her children. I never took issue with pitching in for her if she needed me. As a mother, I appreciated her devotion to her boys and saw how much she struggled to give them a good life. I was preparing to head out for my run when I saw her name appear on my phone. I hesitated only briefly before answering. "Hey Chloe, what's up?"

"Molly! Thank God you answered, nobody else will pick up. Jasper is sick today and I am supposed to be hosting an open house in North Valley today. I don't want to cancel because I really need this house sold, and since it's a Saturday and the weather is nice - " She trailed off. It was probably just another ear infection. She couldn't afford the surgery and he had them at least once a month.

I closed my eyes and groaned silently. Hosting an open house is mostly standing around bored all day, occasionally greeting nosy neighbors and lookie-loos. Frequently there would be large blocks of time where it would be completely deserted. Nobody. Being alone and bored was a breeding ground for introspection, which led to self-loathing. I looked at my tennis shoes in my hand and imagined myself out on the road, running 16 miles, not a single thought in my head. Bliss.

"Okay, I'll do it." *Do what feels right and fuck everyone else.* That's how I got here. I fucked everyone else. Selfish. I tossed my running shoes aside and headed back upstairs, berating myself the entire time. *Stupid. Why did you answer the phone? Gullible.*

Nobody told me that across town a young mother holding her feverish, limp child to her body while listening for the ambulance would offer up a prayer of thanks for a selfless coworker who picked up the phone.

***

My assumption about the curious neighbors was correct. No bona fide buyers crossed the threshold all day. I tried to stay occupied, but it was difficult. By midday there had only been three visitors. I considered closing up as soon as the current batch of rubberneckers hit the sidewalk. It was a woman and her young daughter who were *just looking*, as the mother insisted as she sauntered past me, barely a glance in my direction. So I didn't bother them. I heard a sound from behind me and turned to find the little girl smiling up at me.

"Hello," She said shyly. "May I please have a glass of water?"

I smiled at her unexpectedly formal way of speaking. She had light brown hair that curled just below her shoulders and her dress clearly was taken from a box of dress-up clothes. It had pink ruffles with sparkles and sequins covering the entire upper half. Avery used to wear these as well. She would insist on keeping it on while we went grocery shopping, not unlike Jason's Spiderman costume. *Let them wear the costume.*

I handed her a small bottle of water from the refrigerator. "I love your dress! Where did you get it?" She beamed. I know how much children enjoy being spoken to like adults.

"My closet!" She said excitedly. I chuckled at her answer. "I have four more just like it, but one is blue with sparkles, one is purple with ruffles all over here -" She waved her hand over her arms to indicate the sleeves. "- and I have a yellow one that I don't like so much, but that's because Margot at school said it's ugly."

I rolled my eyes and leaned down close to her and whispered, "I bet Margot's ugly."

She giggled and threw her hand over her mouth and nodded. "Do you live here?" She asked me.

I told her I was just helping someone sell the house to a family who needs one. I asked her what she thought about the house. It wouldn't be the first time a house was sold because of a child's input. She shrugged and said, "It's okay, I guess." I smiled. Talking to this little girl was the highlight of my day so far. My week, honestly. Maybe even the whole summer.

"If you were to buy a house, what would you want in it?" I asked her.

She considered the question for a minute, then started, "Well, first of all, I would have a room filled with balls, you know like at McDonald's, and there would be no stairs, only escalators and slides. Also, I would have a room filled with puppies. I would have a giant fish tank, but not for fish, it would be for my mermaids." I smiled and nodded, encouraging her to continue. She glanced quickly behind her and went on in a quieter voice, nearly a whisper, "All of the doors in the house would be very, very small, so no grownups could come in." Before I could process that last part, what it meant, we were startled by a loud voice.

"Josephine!" The little girl jumped. "Stop bothering the lady, adults do not want to listen to this nonsense, let's go." She grabbed her hand and yanked her out of the room. The little girl waved sadly at me.

As I watched the sparkly young lady with the sad face disappear around the corner and I thought about Jason. I remembered a particular day when Jason marched his tiny 3-year-old body right up to a man with a motorcycle helmet and asked him if that was his Goldwing in the parking lot. The man was unsure at first how to respond to this miniature Harley expert in front of him. It was unusual to see a 3-year-old speak that much, let alone about specific motorcycle brands. Fortunately, the man didn't dismiss him or ignore him, he spoke to him like an adult, and when he walked away he said *That's quite a kid you got there.* Yes, it was.

Do what feels right.

I grabbed a pen and paper and raced after the woman and child. "Excuse me!"

She stopped at the door, a look of impatience blanketing her face. The little girl's face was white as a sheet.

I crouched down next to her and said, "Josephine, is it? I'd like to write down your ideas so that I can get the supplies ordered, I'm afraid I'll forget. Can you tell me again?"

Her face lit up. "I like to be called Josie!" She then repeated her dream house requirements. I took care to write each down, asking questions as we went, taking it very seriously.

"How big do you think the mermaid tank should be? As big as the house, or maybe just the wall?"

When my list was complete I handed her my card. I told her that someday when she's ready to buy a house of her own to let me know and I'd be happy to help her with her needs. She was glowing. I wanted to say so much to the mother, *let her talk, let her imagination go wild*, but I wasn't in any place to pretend to be a good mother. I shouldn't be giving anyone advice. I was a bad mother. Nobody told me that the truly bad mother just walked out the door.

CHAPTER 30 - THE WRONG TIME

Two weeks into July, Sophie and I had already thrown ourselves into business planning. There was so much to do. Meetings with banks, lawyers, city officials, contractors; picking suppliers, a delivery vehicle, a suitable location, a business name. She had already put in her notice and had cut down her hours until her last day. This was her dream and she was full steam ahead. Jane was obviously limited in her physical abilities after her accident, but she was not short on input.

Even with Jane's investment check and Sophie's savings, we would need to secure a business loan in order to make this happen. I wanted to avoid that avenue as much as possible. If the business failed, I didn't want to find ourselves under a mountain of debt, especially after Jane and Sophie invested so much of their own money. Walter and Margaret Green were the clients that had been hounding me for months and nearly derailed my New York trip. They still hadn't found a house or a suitable agent, so I made the decision to take them on and use whatever commission I received from the sale and use it as my contribution. It meant I would never even touch our joint savings account, let alone a bank loan. I knew that would please Scott.

We found a suitable commercial spot to lease right here in town. We met with a contractor about putting in a drive-thru window so meals could be picked up on the go, as well as many other remodeling projects and upgrades that were needed, including a large professional-grade kitchen.

When I spoke with Jason and Avery about it, they were really supportive of the idea. They even volunteered to help with delivery when they came home to visit during the holidays. We anticipated that those weeks would be our busiest. Scott had been supportive as well, but I felt as if he were treating it like a cute little activity to keep me busy. It didn't sit right with me. He didn't directly say anything, but when I gave him updates he sometimes didn't even take his eyes off the TV. I just stopped talking about it altogether.

The Greens were coming to town later in the week and I had multiple showings scheduled. With any luck, I would be done within a week and have my commission check sent directly to our business account by next month.

***

On Monday I woke up in a great mood. I still had a few days until the showings and Sophie was at her office meeting with some of her clients to wrap up the last of her cases. I woke up early and did a 7-mile run, then went to the gym and did a few laps in the pool. I still somehow was full of energy, so I spent the remainder of the day cleaning, baking, singing along to music, responding to Sophie's constant texts. We were meeting at the Salty Dog later to go over some business, but she couldn't seem to wait until then. I brought some of my baked goods to Jane. She was healing and Sophie and I took turns at her house, along with a home health nurse.

I was standing at the sink finishing up the dishes from my baking spree when a voice from behind startled me. "Gordon said you've started working again?" Scott had come home for lunch and I didn't hear him over the running water and the music. I nodded. Before I could explain he continued, "What about that other thing, with Sophie?" I bristled at that statement. Did he call it a *thing*?

"I agreed to go back before I agreed to partner with Sophie, but other than covering for some of the other agents when needed, I've only taken on one big client. I was planning on finalizing them and putting in my notice before the grand opening of our *thing*." I used air quotes, even though he hated them so much. "The client I took on is a couple with a very high budget that I started showing in April, the ones that made me late for the flight, but I've been putting them off ever since because I wanted to honor your request to quit -"

"-take a sabbatical" He interrupted.

I glared at him for interrupting. "Anyway," I continued. "Gordon said they kept requesting me, but I turned it down out of respect for you and your request that I take a *sabbatical*." I used the air quotes again, quite sarcastically I realized too late.

"You should have at least talked to me about it," He pointed out. "Why didn't you just finish it up after we got back from New York in April? That money would have been helpful when we paid for Jason's move and furnishing his apartment. We used quite a chunk of our savings for that."

"We used *MY* savings," I said, more irritated than ever. "All of that money came from the commissions I earned for Avery to use at Columbia." I picked up the sponge and began aggressively scrubbing a pan. "You were pretty clear that you didn't want me to continue working, that we didn't need the money and you wanted me to focus on my family. If you thought we needed the additional income you shouldn't have asked me to quit." I used that word on purpose, waiting for the correction that didn't come.

"I didn't know you were going to suggest we finance his entire move, including first and last month's rent and furnishing the entire apartment." I stopped my hand mid-scrub and turned slowly to face him, a raging fire burning in my ears. He continued to spew gasoline on my anger. If you had discussed the client with me and told me how much money you wanted to throw at Jason's move, I would have encouraged you to keep working, keep showing, but you didn't. It wouldn't have been that big of a disturbance in our life, how difficult could it be to sell one house?"

How difficult could it be?

"How difficult could it be to draw one house, Mr. Fancy Architect?" I was being childish and I hated myself for it, but I was furious. "Since when do I need permission to use my own income? You would have been disappointed if I had continued to work, and I would have suffered even *more* guilt being apart from my family. Every time I missed dinner, all the phone calls I didn't pick up, I would feel how much I let my family down. That's why I didn't do it then."

He stood silent for a minute, staring at the floor "And now?"

I was confused.

He continued, "You've taken on this client, and I don't even know how many others, and now you have this new partnership with Sophie, not to mention the marathon training program, as well as assisting Jane every day. You said you would have felt guilty if you had taken the client back in April because you'd be away from your family. Do you feel that now?"

I turned to face him and said, "I don't know if you've noticed or not, Scott, but the kids don't live here anymore."

He studied my face for a moment and then turned toward the door. Before he walked out he added quietly, "I don't think you've noticed, but I still do."

***

Later that evening when Scott returned, I had prepared his favorite dinner as a peace offering. It's not that I was sorry or apologizing or expecting one from him, I just wanted to get past this and move on with our lives without any tension between us.

At the dinner table, between stories of a new crosswalk in town and Avery's hysterical message to both of us about their experience on the Subway earlier, Scott said "Did you call Gordon and give him your notice?" He continued his meal as if he had not said anything at all.

"No. Why would I?" I asked, holding my fork in midair, frozen.

He looked up at me, completely silent. "No reason; don't worry about it. " He finished his bite and carried his still almost full plate into the kitchen.

"I need to finish what I've started first. That client was only brought on board so I can use the commission as an investment, I told you that." I was extremely frustrated with his attitude about this.

He plopped down at the table. "You're spreading yourself so thin with this new business, marathon training, and taking care of Jane. I didn't realize you'd also be going back to selling houses on top of all of that. I barely see you now. We should have talked about it first. We should have at least discussed the investment. I feel like I've been taken out of the equation. What exactly is my purpose here anymore?" He looked defeated. I felt ambushed, attacked. None of this made any sense to me. Why was this all suddenly about us? I didn't need this kind of stress, he was supposed to be my rock, my support, but he was making my life more difficult.

"Since when did you ever care, need, or even want the financial contribution from my commissions? What was it you called it? Oh yea, a *pastime*. We never discussed clients, income, nor the use of it before, so why do you care now?" I began to clear the dishes; the mostly uneaten dinner I cooked:

"It's not about the money, Molly." He took a step forward. "It's about us. This all seems personal."

"Personal? I don't even know what that means." I grabbed my purse and headed for the door.

"Please, don't go," He said, exasperated. "We need to talk about this."

I stopped and turned to face him. "Now you want to talk. Our kids were leaving and for eight months I was broken and I had to cope with this on my own because you were managing just fine and shut your eyes to anything I felt or needed." I clenched my keys tightly, feeling the negative energy and feelings pour from me like a poisoned fountain. "I'm finally feeling complete again, like I'm making a contribution to someone, somewhere, and it's making me happy. Now you want to talk because you're unhappy."

He suddenly was angry as well. "That's a little dramatic don't you think, and also unfair. We did talk, we talked all the time. What you did or did not say is not my fault."

I just shook my head and grabbed the handle of the door.

He added one more thing, right before I shut the door. "When did you ask me how I felt? I lost my kids too, you know. I was alone then because I saw that you were hurting, and I didn't want to add to your burden. Now I'm alone because you're doing everything you can to avoid me."

I heard what he said, but I didn't listen. I left. Nobody told me that sometimes walking away is the right thing to do. This wasn't one of them.

Chapter 31 - The Second Best Margarita

On my way to The Salty Dog I called Sophie and asked her to meet me there. We had planned to do so later, but I needed to get away from Scott right now. I never had many female friends, but I knew sometimes they complained about their husbands to each other, but I could never do that. Regardless of how upset I was, I have always felt it was incredibly disrespectful. I was pretty angry but I had no intention of speaking ill of my husband to Sophie. I just wanted a break.

I arrived to find her car already parked out front. Once inside I looked around and saw that she was sitting at the bar speaking to Miles. It occurred to me at that moment that I had not introduced them. I wasn't even sure I had ever mentioned him. Sophie dominated most of our conversations.

When she noticed me she shouted, "There she is!" She jumped off her stool and nearly floated to me and grasped my hands. "I want you to meet someone!" She lowered her voice, "He's so adorable. I come here all the time just to see him." She giggled like a schoolgirl and blushed. She tugged my arm and I followed her over to be introduced to my little brother who was smirking. Sophie seemed so proud of herself. "Molly, this is Miles, he's the bartender here. He makes the best margaritas in town, do you want one?"

I kept my eyes locked on Miles, aware that he was intending to enjoy this just as much as I was. He pointed at me and said to Sophie, "This is the friend you've been telling me about?" Her smile faded, but he continued, "I thought you had better taste."

I set my purse down and looked at her seriously, "Honestly, Sophie, *Tequila Mockingbird* down on Pine Street actually has the best margaritas in town. Also, Miles isn't a bartender, he just poses as *Sam Malone* for beautiful women. He's really more of a *Woody*."

The look on her face ranged from alarm to confusion. We both broke character and burst out in laughter. She was too sweet and innocent to deceive for too long. Miles and I laughed so hard we were crying. Finally, Sophie said "I'm not sure who *Sam Malone* and *Woody* are? Do they work here?"

Over the next few hours and many shots and second-best-margaritas-in-town later, Sophie had said *I can't believe you're twins* no less than 10 times, to which I would respond *I can't believe you're too young to remember 'Cheers'*. In the short time we had been friends, and the hundreds of thousands of words Sophie had spoken, I had not registered that she was only 28 years old. It wasn't that she didn't look young, but I had always presumed she was older.

I observed Sophie and Miles over the course of the night. She was clearly smitten with my brother, and the feeling appeared to be mutual. Why had I never considered introducing them before? There is an age difference, but that doesn't have to be a factor. I knew that Miles would likely try to avoid the discussion of his age for as long as possible, but Twin Molly would never let that go untouched.

At one point, Miles went to the other end of the bar to make a drink for a customer. I leaned over and whispered, "We're not really twins, by the way, he just loves his baby sister so much that he tells that to everyone." She looked over at Miles like a puppy dog who just met his best friend. I stood up and went in the direction of the bathroom, aware that I had just placed a landmine.

I heard her say, "How much older than Molly are you?"

"MOLLY!" I heard Miles roar across the room. I laughed and shuffled faster to the women's room.

When I emerged they were huddled together, whispering and laughing about something. "I think I'm going to call an Uber." She grabbed her phone.

"I can drive you," Miles said. Her face brightened. I rolled my eyes. Okay, I can be supportive of this, but it also might make me throw up. The tequila shots didn't help either.

"As much as I'd love to regurgitate the pint of tequila in my gut, I need to interrupt the launch of the love boat and have you take me to Sophie's too." I felt very drunk, I was presently seeing two of my brothers standing in front of me, both of whom exchanged looks with a fuzzy-looking Sophie. "Don't ask any questions, please," I warned him. "I just don't want to go home tonight." I knew my words were slurred, they didn't come out correctly.

"Believe it or not, your Uber has already arrived." Miles grabbed me by the shoulders and propelled me toward the exit. I saw Scott in the doorway wearing his gray sweats, slippers, and a UW sweatshirt. He apprehensively lifted his arm to wave at me.

I whirled around and scowled at all of the brothers I saw, as well as the Fuzzy Sophie. "Traitors," I said to all of them. I hadn't even mentioned the fight we had earlier. How did he know?

What I supposed was probably my actual brother, *Judas* himself, came in for a hug and said softly, "He was concerned and called to see if I had heard from you. Go home and talk to him. I'll look after Sophie."

He shoved me in Scott's direction. "I'll bet you will!" I slurred over my shoulder. I turned back at the last minute and called out, "Don't steal my best friend, Miles!"

Scott steered me to the car. We said nothing on the way home, nor did we speak when we got there. I settled into our bed, which was somehow spinning around our room. I instantly jumped up and ran to the bathroom. In our younger, more carefree life, after a night on the town, Scott would hold my hair if I was throwing up. He didn't even move from the bed. When I returned I knew he had not fallen asleep yet. He was not moving, not speaking. He was disappointed in me. I was angry at him. We were both miserable. We were both lonely. We both remained silent.

Nobody told me that when my husband's heart broke, it didn't make any noise at all.

CHAPTER 32- THE HANGOVER

It goes without saying that I did not wake up in a pleasant mood. I made an effort to knock back some coffee and water, but nothing helped. I relived the previous day with disgust. The client. My job. Scott. The argument. Tequila. Miles. Sophie. Ugh.

A text arrived and I picked up my phone, the brightness at a much higher level than I remembered. *Sophie.*

Hey best friend! I'm going to come by and pick you and Jane up around noon and we will go to the Dog for our meeting about the vendors, vehicles, etc. Jane already knows I'm coming, so can you go help her get ready? Hope you're feeling okay! Tylenol and Water!

Ugh. Her texts were just as long-winded as her verbal exchanges. *Best friend.* I forgot about that. She likely already purchased matching necklaces for us.

I threw on some clothes and attempted to look presentable, but I knew it was just The Salty Dog. Miles had seen me looking much worse than this stack of a hot mess, not to mention it will provide him with more fuel for sibling harassment. My gift of the day. Sophie already declared our forever friendship, she won't mind what I look like, or smell like - I took a quick sniff of my shirt and winced. Maybe I should shower first.

***

I let myself into Jane's house since I knew she was still barely mobile even with her new walker. She nearly met me at the door, a wide smile on her face, dressed as if she were going to Sunday Mass.

"Look at you!" I said. "You're really moving around now."

Her home nurse had been by that morning and had already helped her get ready. Her smile faded when she noticed my appearance. "Oh my, Molly, you look like you slept in a dumpster. Follow me, I'll get you some coffee."

I told her about everything that happened, the fight with Scott, the Salty Dog, Sophie, Miles, drinking, even the puking. She laughed loudly for a very long time afterward. "Bless your silly little heart, Molly." She clapped her hand on my knee and continued to chuckle and shake her head. "Would you like me to top your coffee off with some whiskey, maybe tequila? A little hair of the dog?" I groaned and put my face in my hands and she roared again.

She finally got quiet and serious. "Can I give you a piece of neighborly advice?" I nodded. "On account of the fact that this is your first fight with Scott, perhaps you should go easy on yourself."

I blinked, confused. "This isn't our first fight, Jane."

She snorted and said, "Well, you're certainly carrying on like it is." She stood up and pushed her walker toward the front door. "Put your big girl panties on and talk to Scott like you want to be talked to, listen to him like you want him to listen to you." I followed her to the door. Before I could open it she looked at me and put her hand on my shoulder. "If you treat your marriage like a one-way street, you'll find it's a dead end." She was quiet for a few seconds but kept her hand on my shoulder. Her mind seemed to wander and her eyes teared up. She looked back at me, "Trust me, Molly." I nodded, understanding what she meant. The lump in my throat and the pit in my stomach were worse than the hangover.

The three of us rode to town in Sophie's car. Neither Sophie nor Jane could stop smiling. I wondered if Sophie's smile had anything to do with my brother, her newly minted title of best friend, our business, finally getting Jane out of the house in something other than an ambulance, or just because the happiness inside her was genuine. I tried to remember how that felt, true happiness, when I wasn't trying so hard.

Miles helped escort Jane into the Salty Dog. This was her first time meeting my brother and she was just as enamored as Sophie. She leaned close and said "Do you have any older brothers, by chance, Molly? Maybe an uncle?" I laughed and shook my head.

It was extremely difficult to concentrate on the meeting. It was a good thing Sophie was in control because my mind was swirling and it wasn't just the hangover. I felt like I needed some fresh air, so I excused myself and stepped outside. I walked aimlessly down the sidewalk thinking about the night before, the problems with Scott. We weren't just having a disagreement, there was something genuinely troubling us and it didn't feel right at all. I thought about calling him and offering up an apology, but I wasn't even sure what I was sorry for. I didn't understand what was happening between us.

I stopped at a bench in the local park and watched a little girl on the swing. She was laughing and saying *higher, Nana, higher!* She had light brown hair in pigtails and reminded me so much of Avery at that age; she always wanted to go higher, higher. I noticed that the Nana pushing her wasn't her grandmother after all, it was Hannah. I stood up and walked closer.

"Hannah?" I said, hoping I wasn't intruding.

"Oh!" She jumped, startled by my voice. "Molly! How are you?" She quickly came in for a hug, a little more enthusiastically than the last time, at the coffee shop. "It's so good to see you, this is Jessica, I am working as her nanny for the summer." Jessica waved at me and took off toward the jungle gym.

There was an awkward pause before I spoke again. "Are you going to be teaching at North Valley High in September?"

I watched her look down at her feet and bite her lip. She was silent for several moments before she finally said, "I'm not sure yet. I'm just still a little, um, lost, I guess. I'm not sure what I want to do." She had tears in her eyes, and she looked away, blinking rapidly.

"Oh, Hannah, I'm so sorry." I reached out to touch her shoulder trying to comfort the young girl I'd grown to love so much.

She quickly wiped her eyes and tried to look more positive "Don't worry about me, Molly, I'm fine. I'm just finding that I'm really lonely. I didn't realize how much of my life I had tied up in Jason until he was gone." She called out to Jessica and let her know it was time to go home. I didn't know how to respond to that. I don't want to get in the middle, but maybe if they would just talk to each other she could get some closure. I hesitated for a beat, fighting an internal battle with myself. Before I could make a decision, she grabbed Jessica's hand, waved goodbye, and walked away. I figured it was probably the right thing to do. It wasn't. Nobody could have told me that though. Nobody.

I started back off down the street again. I stopped when I reached the building that housed *Medler Realty. I stood* there for a moment looking at the structure, a 3-story building that also held a dental office and the local newspaper offices. The agent with the top sales in the region every year was the first name on the sign. I had been that agent for 4 straight years. I was proud of that.

I smiled and went inside. It may be one of the last times I would walk in as an employee. I planned to let Gordon know I was done. I would show them one more house and if they didn't want that one, I would resign for good.

I was taking one step in the right direction, an effort to heal whatever pain Scott was feeling that I caused.

Nobody told me it might be too late.

Chapter 33 - The Worst

I was setting the table when I heard a text notification. I checked my phone to see a message from my brother. He had an emergency at the Portland Dog and needed to head out and wouldn't be bringing Pepper with him. He didn't have time to drop her by my house so he asked me to stop by and pick her up. I started a text to Scott; I thought it might be easier for him to swing by there on his way home. I wasn't even done typing when the door opened. He was an hour early. He set his keys and wallet down and went upstairs without a word. I dropped down into a chair at the table and let the tears fall. I was the worst wife in the entire world. He deserved better.

He emerged from the bedroom to eat dinner, but he spoke no words. There were no stories about his clients or coworkers; he didn't ask about the kids or tell me about anything they may have told him; he didn't ask about me or my day. I expected as much. Although it wasn't our first fight, it most certainly was the most distressing. The silence it created in its wake was deafening.

I tried to initiate the conversation, break the ice that was forming between us. "I went to the office today and spoke with Gordon." He didn't even look up or miss a beat in his dinner. I continued. "I told him I wasn't taking any more clients and that if the Greens don't like the house I'm showing them Friday, I'm done for good." He nodded and said *okay*.

My heart sank. I anticipated that this would have made him happy, helped heal our rift. I had banked on things that did not happen. He didn't thank me for resigning. He did not offer a hug. We were not in any way making up or on the path to moving on. Instead of being sad and hurt, I felt anxious and fearful. Maybe there was nothing more I could do to make things right. He continued to eat.

Despite the lump in my throat, I continued, hoping for the best. I noted a small quiver in my voice. "I have high hopes for that house on Friday, it has everything they want." He remained silent as if he never heard me. The house was so quiet I could hear the Robinson's dog barking three houses away. My eyes had welled up with tears, but I couldn't stop trying. I needed to keep on. "I'll be working with Sophie full time after that. Is it okay if I use the commission as my investment?" He said nothing for what felt like an eternity. My breathing had become fast and my heart was pounding. He finished his bite and laid his fork down on the plate.

"If that's what you want to do, that's fine with me." He stood from the table and walked to the sink. My head was spinning. He left the kitchen and started toward the stairs.

"Hey Scott?" I called out. He turned around "Are we okay?"

He didn't answer at first and then said, "Of course." He proceeded up the stairs. He did not come back. Thirty minutes passed, an hour. I did not move from my seat at the table. I tried to ease my anxiety, steady my breathing. I finally decided to check on him and found him in our bed, sleeping. I closed the door quietly and went downstairs. I sat in the dark, empty living room alone and felt the tears flow. How did we get here? How did I get here? My kids are gone. My husband barely even looks at me and now isn't even speaking to me. Lost. Alone. Then I remembered why. Because I'm a selfish, awful person. Since the kids left I somehow had managed to stay busy enough to forget. Too busy for Scott. Too busy to listen. What had I become? The worst. I grabbed my purse and walked out the door.

Nobody told me how lonely rock bottom was.

I let myself into my brother's house and was enthusiastically greeted by Sergeant Pepper. I dropped to my knees and let her kiss my face. "At least someone still likes me," I said to no one in particular. I sat down on the couch and lifted my legs to prop my feet up on his coffee table. Miles had a housekeeping service come in once a week and it clearly was time as it was covered in leftover take-out containers, cans, mail, and magazines. I used my foot to push some cans and magazines off to make room for my feet. I kicked my tennis shoes off and flipped them across the room. I laughed as they hit a wall. This wasn't my house, I didn't have to clean anything. All of the air rushed out of me with an *oof* as Pepper crawled into my lap as if she were a puppy. Miles had no rules about Pepper being on the furniture, mostly because he spoiled her rotten, but also because he usually replaced his furniture every 2-3 years anyway. Even if he did, I would have let her anyway.

I grabbed the remote with one hand and stroked her soft fur with the other. I had to lean far to the left to see the television over my new large furry lap ornament. I flipped through channels aimlessly for a while before I settled on a movie I had seen already, but I knew it would give me comfort and allow me to zone out. I was asleep before I knew it.

I was woken by wet, sloppy kisses. It took me a minute to remember I was at my brother's house, on his couch, being doused in dog slobber. I walked her out the back door and stood on the deck until she had finished her business. It was already a pleasant morning. Miles had a large back yard. The fence was built high enough to keep Pepper in, and I could have gone back inside, but I stayed and enjoyed the nature and the fresh air. He had landscapers come out weekly and keep his yard looking immaculate.

I smiled when I remembered the day last spring when Avery accused me of fantasizing about Scott while he did yard work. She was right, I was. I thanked God we didn't have a landscaper. I loved watching his arms while he moved the weedeater along the fence line, his face while he concentrated on pulling weeds from the garden, and listening to him sing along to his music while he pushed the mower around the yard. He was still so handsome; in fact, he got better every year.

I felt my mood darken when I remembered that he was barely speaking to me. He couldn't even look me in the eye. I shook those memories away and followed Pepper back inside. I started the coffee. I stood at the counter with my eyes closed. I didn't want to think about my life, how many things I had ruined simply by touching them. I let the tears fall, and made no effort to wipe them away.

I had no plans for the day. Training-wise, it was supposed to be a rest day. I didn't actually rest on those days; yoga, swimming, sometimes even a brisk walk were my usual activities. I considered my options and remembered the time Avery brought up hobbies. I couldn't just take up a one-day hobby, could I? I remembered that she mentioned that I should take up hiking. That seemed like a great one-day hobby. Miles and Pepper hiked regularly. How hard could it be?

I looked down at the lab, her beautiful brown eyes staring back at me. "Do you want to go hiking?" She let out a short *woof* and ran for the stairs. I smiled and followed. She knew where Miles kept his hiking gear, I was sure of that. I'll just borrow some and take a fun little day trip. What could go wrong?

***

I grabbed as much of the gear I could and stuffed it into a pack that Pepper pulled out of the closet with her teeth. I didn't know what I should or should not bring on a hike, but I figured if I packed as much as I could find at least I would be prepared. I picked up a water filter. Well duh, I'm going to need to drink water, right? I threw in an umbrella and a poncho; it's the Northwest, you never know. I grabbed a roll of toilet paper and stared at it, confused. Did Miles bring this just in case the bathrooms ran out? I tossed it aside and rolled my eyes. I grabbed a water bottle from the refrigerator, but just one since I obviously packed the filters; I didn't need the excess weight. I threw in a granola bar and an apple for a snack. I wasn't going to be gone *that* long.

I sat down at his desk and opened his laptop. I was going to try to find the best hiking trail. I paused when I came to the password screen. *Oh no.* I didn't know what it was. Or did I? Miles was a simple man. It couldn't be too difficult. I tried *SargentPepper.* Incorrect. I considered other options. I tried his birthday. Incorrect. I typed in *SaltyDog.* Incorrect. These are all too obvious.

I glanced over at the wall to my left and saw a framed photo and leaned in closer. I grabbed the wood frame and gently took it from the wall. It was a picture of us when we were children. We were on the only vacation we had ever taken as children. Knotts Berry Farm. We were wearing matching T-shirts and red shorts. We were playing up the twin thing. Our arms were around each other and we were laughing. We were soaked from head to toe. We went on the ride not realizing that we could get wet, and we ended up getting stuck under a waterfall. I glanced at the password screen again and typed in something I was sure wouldn't work, but wanted to try it anyway. It worked. I felt my eyes sting, blurred with tears. I picked the frame up and held it to my chest. I loved my brother so much, but I sometimes forget that the bond we have goes both ways. He's everything to me, but I have Scott and the kids as well; I go home to them. I'm all he has. I'm all he's ever had.

I blinked away the tears and went to his browser and found a website that listed all of the trails in the area. I found a perfect one. *Redemption Falls;* I could certainly use some Redemption. It was about a 10-mile round trip moderate hike, 3500 feet elevation. I didn't know what that meant exactly, but I ran twice as much than that every week, piece of cake.

I left Miles a note on his kitchen counter indicating that we went on a hike. I didn't want him worrying about his precious pup if he returned before I did. He'd be lost without her.

***

There were four other cars parked at the trailhead when I arrived. It was later than I expected, almost 11:00 a.m. I knew it was going to be a sweltering day, so I figured some of these people set out much earlier than I did just to get a head start on the heat. I didn't consider that, but maybe I should have.

Three miles into the hike I was exhilarated. I couldn't figure out why I hadn't done this more often. We stopped often to take in the incredible views. Pepper and I took many selfies. She stopped to mark her territory on nearly every tree and bush. She wanted to taste every creek and smell every bush. I had initially worried about being alone with my thoughts, and the consequences of that, especially after the revelation that I was not only a terrible mother but a terrible wife. I anticipated that I may have to turn around and run back to my car. I did not. Nature gave me peace. It gave me a reason to look around and see a bigger picture; bigger than me and my behavior and the influence I had on those I loved.

I got to Redemption Falls at 6:00 p.m., which was much later than I had anticipated. I did not take into account that I would walk a little slower while climbing into higher elevations, that the pack would be heavier than I figured, nor that Pepper's hiking expertise was highly exaggerated by my brother. I thought she was going to lead me, but she would lead me right off a cliff if a squirrel did. She had the assumption that every squirrel in the world was her best friend.

I sat on a rock at the base of the falls and ate a granola bar that I had taken from Miles. It tasted as if it expired the day Lincoln was shot. Knowing I didn't pack much food, I choked it down and vowed to buy groceries for Miles tomorrow.

I glanced at the time and did some unfortunate math. It would be dark by the time we got back to the car. Pepper whined as if she heard my thoughts.

I took a final swig of the bottle of water and let Pepper have the remainder. I realized then that I did not have any more water. I was relieved that I remembered the water filters. I pulled them out and went to the creek. The directions were written in a font so small I was sure it was meant for elves and fairies. *Who the hell could read writing that small?* I didn't think to bring my glasses, it was hiking for God's sake, not a crossword puzzle.

Frustrated, I threw the filters and water bottle on the ground and grabbed my pack. I just wasted precious daylight on this.

"Let's go!" I said gruffly to Pepper. She whined and looked down at the mess I made by the creek. I groaned. "Fine, I'll pick up my trash." As I was shoving the useless junk into my pack as fast as I could Pepper sauntered ahead down the trail. "Don't go far, Pepper!"

She returned, her face wet and muddy from drinking from a puddle. "Show off," I said. "I shouldn't have let you have the rest of the water if you were just going to drink mud."

I threw the pack on and gave her head a quick rub. "Let's go home, girl." I was a little nervous, but I didn't want her to see that. At the last minute, I grabbed the headlamp I had seen in the side pocket. I wanted to have it available when it got dark. I hoped the batteries were in better shape than the snacks were.

When I woke up, Molly was gone. She never came to bed and she didn't appear to have slept anywhere else, not in Jason or Avery's room, and not on the couch. Her car was gone from the driveway. I had no doubt that she was at her brother's house. I called my office and took a personal day. I figured it was time to have a serious conversation with Molly and she likely wouldn't return until she thought I had left for the day.

I stared at my blank phone screen and considered calling or texting, but instead laid it down on the table and sipped my coffee trying to figure out exactly what I was going to say to her, what she would say. Where did we make a wrong turn? I could have been a little more understanding of what she was going through, but the truth is that she's the strong one in our family, not me. She was the foundation of this family and when she started wavering and cracking, I was lost as to what to do; she would have known. She never asked for my support, but she needed it. I failed her.

I stepped into the garage and opened the large door, the gears clanking and whirring. I made a mental note to get that fixed. If only marriage were so easy to fix, make a phone call, schedule a repair time.

One of my long avoided projects recently had been to reorganize the garage shelves, boxes that contained Christmas decorations, old toys the kids no longer played with, clothes they grew out of that Molly couldn't bear to part with. The endeavor was emotionally more than I had banked on. After pulling out a box of stuffed animals that Avery used to keep on her bed I found myself weeping. I could picture them in my head now, lined up in order by size, color, and importance. I carried them up to her room, armload by armload, and lined them up just as she would have. Jules the Giraffe was the largest and stayed at the foot of the bed, with Mickey the Monkey in her lap. I remembered saying good night to each one every single night, Dexter the Dog, Chloe the Cat, Annie the Aardvark. I missed her so much.

After they were lined up, I picked up one in the middle. This one was Toby. This particular 'stuffie' as Avery called them had been mine as a child. I gave it to Jason and over time Avery had stolen it from him so many times that he finally just let her have it. I walked across the hall to Jason's room and laid it on his bed. I missed both of them. All three of them.

Behind a box of Jason's old monster trucks, ones he insisted would be worth money someday, I found an old cardboard box - different from the sturdy plastic totes Molly typically used for storage. I climbed onto the stepladder and eased the brittle box toward, stained with moisture and collapsing on one side. The side of the box had faded, smeared black letters that were barely legible anymore *Molly - Personal.*

Confused, I carefully walked it over to the workbench and eased the lid off, the collapsing side of the box finishing its job, spilling faded papers and old time-worn photographs onto the wooden surface. I picked up an envelope, it was a letter from the CWU Financial Aid Department addressed to Molly Eldridge - Her maiden name. I eased the letter out of the envelope and my jaw dropped. Letter after letter, paper after paper pointed to a woman I didn't know. This wasn't the woman I married.

I thumbed through the old photographs; the first one was a woman with two young children on her lap, the second of a man standing next to two young children. I had not seen very many photos from Miles and Molly's childhood, but it was undeniable that I was getting a rare glimpse into a part of her world I was not privy to. She and Miles claimed that their childhood artifacts had been destroyed in an accident.

At the thought of the word *accident*,, my eyes locked onto a newspaper article that had been clipped. My stomach dropped. The collection of articles fluttered to the floor and I walked into the house, closing the rickety large door behind me, leaving all reminders of the 25-year lie I just lived behind me.

***

I sat in the dark living room with a beer in my hand and two empty bottles next to me. The baseball game was long over but I barely noticed. I was trying to wrap my head around what I had discovered earlier. I glanced again at my silent, blank phone screen. Molly had still not called or texted and it had been well over 24 hours since she left the house. I felt like my life had spiraled so far out of control I didn't know which way the tornado was taking me - Oz or Kansas, or neither.

Headlights cut through the darkened living room, indicating a car had pulled into the driveway. I glanced again at the still silent phone, noting that it was 11:30 p.m. I rushed to the door and pulled it open before Molly could get to it, only to find a tall, blonde male version of her standing there.

"You look like shit, man, what the hell?" Miles strolled past me into the living room and noted the darkness and the likely dank smell of a room that someone had been sitting in for hours. "Sorry if I woke you, I just wanna grab Pepper and get home, I'm exhausted." He stood at the bottom of the stairs and hollered up, "Pepper, let's go! Thanks for watching her, Molly, sorry for waking you!" Then he turned back again and yelled, "NOT!"

"They're not here, Miles," I managed to squeak out, already feeling the bottom drop out of my world, scrambling for it to remain intact.

As he turned to face me I saw his face drain of color, the sudden realization that the two people he cared most about in the whole world were gone.

Chapter 35 A- The Very Long Night By Molly

I tried to make double-time on the way back, but for some reason, Pepper had found even more squirrels, but also chipmunks, birds, and even the phantom wildlife that she needed to chase back to their homes. It had become exhausting. I had a leash in the pack, but I felt that it would be more of a hindrance since Pepper was at least twice as strong as I was.

It had started to become dark. Darkness fell much faster in the woods. Maybe it was my imagination. I stopped to secure the headlamp and turn it on. It was nice and bright, which I was glad to see since I never checked to see if it worked. I wasn't sure there were extra batteries, so hopefully, this would last until we got to the car.

We pressed on. The darkness seemed to make Pepper concentrate a little more on the trail and stick a little closer to me. I wasn't sure how long it had been, or how far, but Pepper let out a loud bark and ran off. She ran fast. I walked out into the bush calling her name. She didn't come. I continued on.

I called out, "Pepper, I swear to God, get your ass back here or I'll make sure Miles never feeds you pizza again." Nothing. I was starting to get worried. I continued on, stopping every once in a while to listen. I heard the occasional bird, the rare tree limb snapping, sometimes the faint hum of an airplane, but no Pepper. Nothing. I pulled my phone out of my pack. This might be a time to call Miles. He was going to be furious at me for taking his dog into the woods without permission, and even more so for losing her. No service. Dammit. What the hell was I supposed to do now?

My phone said it was 10:00 p.m. It's been four hours since I left the falls, maybe I was closer to the car than I thought. I could just go to the car where I had cell service and call for help and hope someone would come and help me find Pepper before Miles disowned me. I stuffed the phone back and turned to head back toward the trail again, trying to move faster even than before. I needed to get there and get help. It was already dark and I was afraid, both for myself and for her. I would disappoint my brother, and I had already disappointed so many others.

I stopped at a fallen log and looked around. I didn't remember seeing this log or anything else in this area. This was the way I came in, right? I hadn't found the trail yet, but I did walk for quite some time after leaving it when I was looking for the dog. I started to panic. The forest was so dense and I did not have a compass, not that I knew how to use one or which of those directions my car or the trail might be. I kept walking anyway. I had to find my way out eventually, right? My foot caught a root and I fell forward. I hit the forest floor with a loud thud. *Shit, that hurt.* I sat up and assessed the damage the best I could in the limited light. I was bleeding from the kne3 and upper leg for sure. Things were hurting in other places, but my leg was the only thing that seemed to have an actual open wound. I knew Miles had a first aid kit in his pack, but I really didn't want to waste any more precious battery time with the headlamp. Just before I stood up I was greeted by the Overconfident Squirrel Hunter.

"Pepper!" I hugged her tight. I wasn't sure if I was angry at her for running off or happy to see her. I realized that it didn't matter. My vision blurred for a moment and I worried I may have a concussion. I wiped my fingers over my eyes and realized that it was blood. My scalp was bleeding and it had dripped into my eyes. Great. That's a problem.

I grabbed the pack again and readjusted the headlamp onto my now tender, bleeding forehead. I winced but made sure it was in place and tight; if it fell and I lost it, there would be even bigger trouble on my horizon. It was pitch black beyond the beam.

I secured Pepper's leash. She was looking at me with sad eyes. "It's for your own good, sweet girl; Miles would be lost without you." I considered the word *lost* and remembered how lost we were. I honestly had no idea where I was or how to get back. I pulled in a very shaky breath, closed my eyes and hoped for the best.

Nobody told me I was in for a very, very long night.

CHAPTER 35 B - THE SEARCH - BY MILES

I committed nearly every moving violation on the drive back to my house. My hands shook and my knuckles were white as I gripped the steering wheel. I only knew three things: The first was that they weren't at my house; the second was that they also weren't at their house; the third was tjat I couldn't imagine what I would do if either of them, let alone both of them, were gone. My heart pounded and I could feel the scar on my leg begin to burn and throb. I absentmindedly began to rub my hand on my leg, trying to ease the pain and distract myself. I had lied to Molly. I didn't go to Portland for work; I had to see a specialist. I shook my head to clear the memory of the results. None of that mattered if Molly was gone. I should have told her. She would have been with me. She would have been safe.

My truck barrelled into the driveway spraying gravel in every direction. Scott was out of the truck before it even stopped moving and was pounding on the front door, "Molly? Are you in there? Open up!!! Please?" I could hear the emotion in his voice, making the word *please* erupt in a high-pitched squealing noise, sobs tearing through him. I could have sworn I heard him say *I'm so sorry* through the closed door.

In the meantime I limped my way up the porch stairs as fast as I could, cursing so many things. I was grateful that my brother-in-law was distracted by the closed-door confessional he was participating in because he wouldn't notice my sudden disability. Something I had kept from nearly everyone for the last 27 years.

Except for the two people who were missing. I shuffled faster, unlocking the door and allowing Scott to rush in past me, calling out for his wife. I made a beeline for the kitchen, knowing Molly would have left me a note on the whiteboard.

Hey, Milo

Took Pepper for a hike, will prob be home before you so disregard

Love Mols

"SCOTT!" I yelled out the back door as he looked under bushes and over the fence. *Hold that enthusiasm, man, you're gonna need it*, I thought.

By the time he barrelled into the kitchen, I had already activated the locator on Pepper's collar, chastising myself for not doing that sooner. They were near Redemption Falls.

The drive to the trailhead was an hour, I made it in 30 minutes. According to the tracker in Pepper's collar they were not far from the trailhead, but grossly off-trail, which meant traversing some possibly dense brush in the deep dark of night. There wasn't even a moon tonight and the evening was so cloudy there weren't even stars to help guide us.

The other thing that kept eating at me was the fact that the location of Pepper's tracker hadn't moved since I first activated it. This can mean a lot of things, and none of them are good. They could be hurt, or worse. The collar could have fallen off somewhere, meaning the search would be widened indefinitely. I began to rub my scar harder, making the already long, painful, jagged line down my thigh scream in pain. Don't you dare slow me down today.

Out of the corner of my eye, I saw Scott in the passenger seat staring at me. His face was illuminated by the occasional street light. He had been awfully quiet since leaving my house. I had so many questions. How was he not aware of his wife's location for an entire day? Why did he say he was sorry?

"What's wrong with your leg?" He asked finally. "Was it the accident? Is that why Molly dropped out of college?"

I groaned. Is that why they were fighting? I figured if she was going to finally make the decision to tell him, she'd warn me first. "Did Molly tell -" I began to say.

"I found a box in the garage," He said. "It had articles and letters, but they just gave me more questions than answers. Why would she lie to me?"

I took a corner faster than necessary, trying to outrun this conversation more than anything. "Molly's decision not to tell you had more to do with me than you or her." I paused, reliving some of the harder times in my head. "I went through a lot back then, and I wouldn't have gotten through it if it wasn't for my sister. She was, and still is, my rock, my everything." A deer jumped in front of the truck, making me slam on the brakes, nearly sending the truck sideways, but thankfully missing the doe and the two fawns that shortly followed. "But what happened back then, what I went through, what she went through? I don't want to relive that ever again. I don't want to see the pain that I saw in her eyes every day. So we moved on."

I slowed down a bit and avoided a very large pothole. "She didn't tell you about college because she dropped out to take care of me, and if she told you she had gone to school but dropped out, she may have had to also explain the reason. You can ask her about it if you want, but just remember everything she did was for me. And she didn't lie to you, she just didn't tell you a story that wasn't hers to tell. She did it out of love. She does everything out of and for the love of her family, you know that. Just don't be angry with her. She doesn't deserve that."

He was silent for a long time. "So, what happened exactly?"

I sighed. "I'll answer anything you want, but no until you talk to Molly, hear her story." I turned the truck down the final stretch before the trailhead, a bumpy road densely shrouded in the forest.

"What if it's too late-" Scott sobbed. I looked sharply at him, daring him to finish that sentence. The one that would finish me as well. "Maybe we should have called the police?" He said.

As some of the brush lightened I saw bright lights, flashing lights. My stomach dropped. I punched the gas, ignoring the potholes and bumps, and sent my truck flying ahead, bouncing down the road like a kangaroo.

The EMT and Search and Rescue teams were standing next to Molly's car. I flew out of the truck toward them frantically yelling. "Is she okay? Where is she?"

They went on to explain that the SOS beacon had been activated and they were just preparing to head in. I said a silent prayer of thanks that she hadn't removed it from the pack; however, I knew she didn't push it on purpose, and since the tracker on Pepper's collar hadn't moved still, she likely fell.

Ignoring the searing pain in my leg, I turned on my headlamp and sprinted down the trailhead, a flashlight in one hand and the tracker in the other. I could hear Scott hot on my heels. The Search and Rescue team hollered after us about safety and lights and I don't know what else because we were gone. I had to find my sister. *Take care of each other until I get there, please.*

Chapter 36 A- The Redemption Path - By Molly

It was dark; so, so dark. I made the ridiculous decision to hike on a new moon night, so there was no light whatsoever. I worried that my headlamp batteries would give out. It was already in the backpack I took from my brother's house. I didn't think to check the batteries or check for extras in the pack.

I remembered hearing that if you find yourself lost that you should stay where you're at, not to move. I couldn't remember why and I couldn't imagine sitting down on a log and just waiting. Waiting for what? Rescue? Did anyone even know I was here? I left a note for Miles that Pepper and I went hiking, but I didn't mention where. Even if they did find out where I was, how far off the trail were we? Then I realized that we could be walking even farther off the trail. I stopped. That's probably why they say to stay put, so you don't get more lost.

My foot hit a patch of something wet and unstable and before I knew it I was on my butt. I began to sob. Pepper plopped down in front of me and put her head in my lap and let out a little whine.

"What are we going to do, Sarge?" I stroked her head. She didn't respond. I wished she could talk. I felt like she'd have the best advice. I wondered briefly what she would think about who I had become. She loved my kids, loved Scott. Would she be disappointed in me too?

I thought about getting up, moving on, but I was feeling a little dizzy; I had not had any water in hours and I had only eaten a granola bar today. I had no idea what time it was; my phone, which had no service anyway, died long ago. I did know that it was dark. I did know that I was lost; very, very lost. I chuckled to myself when I realized the irony. As a mother, a wife, a woman, I was also lost and had been for quite some time. And now I was literally lost.

The forest was incredibly quiet, something I had been trying to avoid, trying to keep my thoughts at bay. Now it was just me and the reminder of how badly I fucked up.

There was suddenly a noise nearby; a twig snapped, bushes rustled. My heart began to pound. Pepper's ears perked up and she let out a small whine. I laid my head back on the tree and closed my eyes. It might be a cougar or a mountain lion. Maybe a bear. It was probably a tiger. Avery liked tigers. I was so tired. I was incredibly thirsty. I felt myself fading. Was I falling asleep, or was I dying? Was there a difference? Did I care? Either way, it was welcome.

I murmured an apology to Pepper for bringing her.

I offered up a silent plea to Miles. *Take care of my family. Tell them I'm sorry.*

I thought of Scott, Avery, and Jason. *I'm so sorry, I should have done better. I should have been better.*

I drifted off.

Chapter 36 B - The New York War - By Avery

It turns out that a brother and sister should not live in a small apartment together, that was determined after the *Why'd You Eat My Yogurt Incident*, and then again after the *Who Used All The Hot Water Debate*, further cemented after the *You Lost Your Key It's Not My Fault Debacle* and finalized by the *No Guests Policy Breach*.

Two weeks before I moved into Columbia I packed my bags and moved into Caitlin's penthouse. Fuck him. He had become such an asshole since moving to New York, I didn't even recognize my brother anymore.

Life with Caitlin wasn't much better, she was a complete snob about anything that wasn't designer or personally recommended by some Instagram Influencer. She spent so much time researching what she should wear and buy and do based on what other people told her to do, and then doing her own influencing videos on YouTube and Instagram based on the same recommendations, it was exhausting.

She was in the middle of filming a YouTube makeup tutorial that would *revolutionize the eyeshadow application forever* when I saw my Mom's friend, Sophie, was calling me. I ran out of her room as fast as I could, trying to avoid her glares of disapproval.

"What's up?" I said breathlessly when I arrived at the safest place to answer.

"It's you mom, Avery." I dropped my phone and heard it shatter.

***

The only thing Caitlin loved more than telling people what they should and shouldn't do, is being the hero. Upon hearing the news and seeing my shattered phone, she got straight to work. She sent one of her mother's assistants to purchase me a new phone. In the meantime, I tried to reach Jason on Caitlin's phone. After the 7th voice mail, each angrier by the minute, I decided I was just going to go to his apartment. It was Saturday, he wasn't at work.

Caitlin called for her driver. In the car on the way I had her call Hannah, because if he would answer for anyone, it would be her.

"She's not answering either, Avery, should I leave a message?" She asked.

I was beginning to feel a rage burn in me. My mother had been there for us every single day of our lives and the one time she needed us, neither Jason nor Hannah could be bothered. "NO!" I yelled, "Fuck her too, then."

I didn't wait for the town car to stop completely before jumping out and running for the door. I still had a key for the building, but I had lost my apartment key, one of our many fights that resulted in Operation Exile Avery.

At Jason's door, I began pounding my fists. "DAMMIT JASON, OPEN THE DOOR!"

pound, pound, pound

Nothing.

"I'LL BREAK THE FUCKING DOOR DOWN, YOU KNOW I WILL!" I could hear the neighbor's doors opening, Caitlin offering up excuses and apologies for me.

I took a few steps back and went for it.

Chapter 37 A - The Tiger By Molly

I drifted in and out. Pepper never left my side. She let out an occasional whimper, but I couldn't move to lift my hand up to comfort her, and I felt guilty about that. So much guilt. I closed my eyes again.

I thought of Avery and Jason. I thought of their smiles, their laughter. I remembered a time long ago, Avery was only six. She was upset with me, but I can't recall why. She said she was going to run away. She even packed her bag and went to the door. Jason said *I'm mad too, I'm running away with you.* Jason was 12 years old at the time and he walked hand in hand with his sister down the street, a suitcase in each hand. About 30 minutes later they returned and Avery hugged me and said she was sorry. She said that Jason told her things that *changed her life.* I thought of that as I drifted off again. At least they would take care of each other.

I dreamed of Scott, the day we met. The spilled beer, the music, the laughter. The blip in time that changed the lives of so many people. My heart had been so full all these years, all of which was because of one man's love for me. And I failed him. I hoped he would forgive me over time.

I woke to Pepper licking my face. I tried to force a smile. Sweet Sergeant Pepper. Miles. I drifted off again with the memory of the day I rushed into the hospital room to find my brother unrecognizable. The bandages, the casts, the tubes, the medically induced coma that lasted for 26 days. The agony I felt tore my soul to shreds, and I still couldn't remember the day without feeling the air rush out of my body. I hoped my brother would be spared the pain of seeing me like that. Maybe that tiger would finish me off before then.

I could have sworn I heard my name, but tigers can't talk, can they? Pepper let out a bark. *Run, Pepper, Run,* I thought. *The tiger wants me, not you.*

CHAPTER 37 B - THE NEW YORK LET DOWN - BY JASON

I had forgotten to shut the curtains in my room when I got home at 2:00 a.m. I don't know why I went out in the first place, I couldn't afford it and I certainly had no business in my state of mind to try to have a good time. The was no such thing as a good time when I was involved, just ask Avery or Hannah. Or anyone.

I could hear my phone buzzing on and off for the last couple of hours. I knew it must be Avery, calling or texting to chew me out for what a shitty brother I've been. I should have handled all of this differently, it wasn't her fault. Moving to New York was a terrible idea. The job is a small step above mail boy. I've seen several people advance in the month since I've been here, and most of them were less qualified or hired more recently than I was. The pay was lower than they had offered, and I had not been able to pay my rent yet this month. My account was so low I wasn't sure how I'd feed myself, let alone Avery. So we fought. And she left.

My head was pounding. I should not have drank so much. Wait, was that my head or was that the door? I lifted my head slightly to hear my sister's threat to break the door down. She wouldn't. I lay back down and throw my pillow over my head as I hear wood splinter. I throw myself out of bed and scramble to the door, throw it open just as Avery tumbles through it, my neighbor's umbrella stand in her hand, a giant hole forming in my door.

"What the fuck, Avery?" I yanked the heavy, damaged wood structure from my sister and handed it back to Mrs. Pedakis, who was standing in the hall wearing only a robe and a look of horror on her face. I mouthed an apology, but she just quickly retreated through her own door, engaging the lock quickly.

I turned to face yet another battle with my sister, but her face, streaked with tears, white as a ghost, stopped me cold in my tracks. But it was what she said that flipped my world.

"We gotta go home, it's mom."

CHAPTER 37 C - THE RESCUE - BY SCOTT

I was breathing heavily. I wasn't a runner, not like my wife. I was so proud of her. I couldn't wait to watch her run the marathon in Boston. Hopefully, she still could. She had to be okay. I pushed past the breathlessness and ran faster, trying to keep up with Miles. Even with the limp, I had a difficult time keeping up with him. I could hear the members of the Rescue Team coming up behind us, see their lights as they swept through the bushes and trees off the trail, hear them calling her name, as well as Pepper's.

Miles veered to the left, cutting through some bushes. I followed after him, snagging my clothes on twigs, stepping over rotting logs. *Where were they? Why were they so far off the trail?* I called her name again, "Molly! Can you hear me? Pepper!" Suddenly I heard a bark, and Miles yelled back to me that he found them.

I ran in the direction of Miles, his flashlight waving me in the right direction. Finally, someone showed me the way.

Then I saw her. Her brown hair illuminated in the dim light, almost camouflaged in the forest floor. She lay still on the ground, unmoving. Her hair was matted with dried blood and pieces of twigs and pine needles. Her face had streaks of blood and a small bruise forming on her forehead. Her lips were cracked and chapped. Her pants were ripped, the material dark and stiff with dried blood.

I needed to see her move, see her smile. I wanted her to forgive me so we could heal together, both figuratively and literally. I wanted nothing more than to spend the next century by her side, but more importantly, I wanted to spend the immediate future making everything right again.

I dropped to my knees and wept. Miles put his hand on my shoulder, he already had Pepper on her leash and had poured some of his water into a collapsible bowl he pulled from the pack. "She's alive, Scott, I think she just got dehydrated and fell." He turned toward the direction of the trail and hollered to the Rescue Team.

"But she's bleeding!" I managed to say between sobs. I reached underneath her, placed my arms under her shoulders and knees and gently picked her up.

The team arrived at that time and said, "Sir, please put her down, we need to examine her before we mobilize her." They had many bright lamps they were setting up so they could have better visualization for their examination. I ignored their pleas as I carried my wife toward the trail, toward home.

I heard Miles behind me talking to the crew, explaining that I was her husband and that she was in good hands. "He'll take good care of her, I promise," He added.

She stirred in my arms, snuggled into my chest. "I promise," I whispered to Molly.

Chapter 38 - The Way Back

I felt hands underneath me. I heard my name. I was lifted off the ground. My head rested against someone. That smell. It was familiar. My name again. That voice. The man I loved. I tried to say his name back. I couldn't. I leaned into him and rested, finally feeling safe.

I opened my eyes and it was incredibly bright. I didn't realize there were lights in the forest, that would have been helpful earlier. I should find out where the light switch was, in case I come back. I drifted off again.

"Molly, can you hear me?" I didn't recognize that voice. I thought I heard Scott earlier, maybe I was just dreaming. Did this person live in the woods? Is he rescuing me or kidnapping me? Did it matter? "Can you squeeze my hand?" I heard the voice say again. I felt someone's skin under my palm. I tried to squeeze this stranger's hand, but I was pretty sure I wasn't. "Great job, Molly, you're doing great." He said again. I tried to laugh. I was doing great? Hardly.

"Is she awake? Can I come in?" That voice was familiar. The man who helped me raise my babies, gave me my home, and everything I've ever wanted or needed. The man I crushed. I felt another palm under my right hand. I didn't even have to open my eyes to know that skin, that touch. I turned my face slightly, and despite the brightness of the forest, or wherever I was, I needed to see his face, his green eyes, his incredible smile, the face of the man I stared at for 2 hours before I took a chance and walked up to him just to hear his voice, and then I spilled my beer on him. He married me anyway. I opened them slightly, hoping to not be assaulted by the brightness, only to be comforted by his smile. The smile that I remembered seeing after our children were born, after we said our vows; before, during, and after every single memory I have. A smile I haven't seen in some time. His beautiful green eyes were filled with tears and his cheeks were streaked with what were probably hours of worry, fear, and sadness. "Thank God," He sobbed. "I love you, Molly; please stay with me."

I would. Forever.

Nobody told me that you can always find your way back as long as you are willing to try. I was less than a mile from the trailhead, and we were on the road to healing.

CHAPTER 39 - THE HOSPITAL

I woke to the sound of snoring. I turned to find my brother, the big man that he is, stuffed into a tiny chair next to the hospital bed, head leaned back, snoring loud enough to wake every patient on the floor. I reached over with my IV laden arm and poked him.

He jerked awake and when he saw me, he softened. "Mols, you're awake." He put his big hand on mine and then jerked away when he felt the IV tubes. I laughed and laid my hand on top of his instead. "Everyone in this hospital is awake thanks to the deviated septum you refuse to get fixed."

"I've had enough of hospitals." He smiled nervously as his eyes darted around. I squeezed his hand and he brought his attention back to me. "I know you have too, Mols, I promise I'll get you home soon." He glanced back toward the door and then back at me and said, "Speaking of home, I'll be right back." He stepped out the door and took a left.

I closed my eyes, feeling a little numb from whatever pain killer they gave me. My right leg had to have several stitches, as did the cut on my scalp and one on my forehead. My hands were bandaged as well from catching my fall. Nothing was broken though. Just my heart, but that was my fault.

A few minutes later I heard the door open. I expected Miles to have returned, hopefully with some ice chips or Jell-O, but when I opened my eyes I saw the three people who charted the map of my soul. They all stood there smiling at me. Scott's arms were looped around each kid. Jason's eyes were bloodshot as if he had been crying for hours. Avery rushed to my side, buried her face in my neck, sobbing. Jason and Scott approached the other side. My son looked so much like a little boy again, unsure of his surroundings. His voice cracked as he said, "Mom, are you okay?"

I looked at Scott, who looked down at me with a smile as bright as the sun and a love as strong as the day we stood under the arch and made a lifelong promise.

"I am now," I said.

Epilogue - The Salty Reindeer Run

It was Christmas morning. My emotions had been pretty difficult to contain all day. Avery and Jason were home for the holiday break. Our business, My Personal Chef, had taken off like a rocket and we had been thrown into a frenzy trying to keep up with orders. Luckily, my kids were more than happy to help out, at a price, of course.

I looked at Sophie, her face flushed with happiness and her smile contagious. She winked at me and looped her arm through my brother's. We shared a secret about the true reason for her rosy cheeks. A true Christmas morning miracle. I never thought I'd be an auntie.

I had been so upset when I found that I would be unable to compete in the Boston Marathon. The tissue damage in my leg had been more extensive than they originally thought and I required surgery to repair some of it and spent 6 weeks in extensive physical training.

It was then that I learned that Miles also had been dealing with complications from his accident all those years ago. Along with posttraumatic arthritis in the hip and knee of that leg, the slight shortening and malrotation have caused extensive nerve damage. We attended our physical therapy sessions together, often heckling each other from across the room. Our scars, while his still much longer and deeper, are nearly identical. After seeing mine, he said *I told you we were twins, Molly.*

I watched my brother stand with his arm around Sophie, talking to Jane, who was sitting on a motorized scooter that he had personally decorated to look like Santa's sleigh. He was showing her how he had rigged up different buttons for her to push that played different songs, noises, or phrases through a megaphone on the front of the scooter. She clapped her hands in glee and beamed at Miles.

When I had to cancel my participation in the race and cease marathon training, Miles began to plan The Salty Reindeer Run- a Christmas Day 5K in our own little town of Medler. He promised eventually we would heal together and train for a marathon, and next year we'd run all the way to North Valley and back. I loved his optimism, but he didn't know yet it would be his baby's first Christmas. That would change everything.

I stood in the brisk air, my Santa hat tucked low over my ears, while the town prepared for the First Annual Salty Reindeer Run. Everyone was dressed as either Santa, a reindeer, or an elf. I waved at Chloe and her two boys. She was dressed as Mrs. Claus and her boys were both dressed as Rudolph. I could assume they both demanded to be Rudolph, so there were two Rudolphs.

I saw my own two kids standing together laughing. Avery and Jason had matching Christmas onesies on and red tennis shoes. Any strife they had back in New York had long been forgotten. Avery was thriving at Columbia, being amongst her peers. She had even started dating someone. She could hardly keep from smiling when her phone lit up.

Jason was doing better. He opened up finally about his struggles in New York. We were able to help him some, but also get him connected with some resources to allow him to branch out on his own, figure out what he's meant to do, where he's meant to be. His eyes met mine and he smiled, lifted his hand up in a quick wave. He would be okay. If not, he could always come home. He knew that. That gave both of us the peace of mind to help us sleep at night.

We stood together in a row, all of us in Santa hats and various costumes and Christmas-themed outfits. Avery and Jason stood to my right, pretending to fight over who would get off the finish line first. Scott stood to my left, his hand gripping mine. I squeezed it and he turned to look at me, leaned in for a kiss. *Merry Christmas, Mols.* He whispered.

Jane stood to Scott's left, hand in hand with Miles, who stood next to Jane. She sat in her scooter and pretended to rev her engine. He dramatically jumped in front of her, pretending as if she were going to run him over.

I heard their laughter and I closed my eyes. This line of amazing humans is everything I ever needed in this world. The mother, wife, sister, friend, the woman I was, and still am, was always enough for them, my doubts were not their doubts. I am still enough for all of these people, and they are everything to me.

The race began, and the crowd began to move. The seven of us walked together, side by side, nobody faster or slower than the next, nobody getting lost in the crowd or losing their way. Nobody told me I had this ability the entire time, to work as a team, to cross the finish line together, arm in arm. I wish somebody had told me.

ACKNOWLEDGEMENTS

This book would never have existed without the encouragement from my brother Kevon, as well as his incredible belief in me and my abilities. Your support is everything.

My family, Joel, Dylan, and Madelyn, who were incredibly patient with my typing, clicking, late nights, and mental and physical absences, as well as their willingness to allow me to use them as inspiration.

Jacqueline Cleveland, my impromptu model for my cover photo. She was in the right place at the right time and had the right look and vibe. Her patience with my request to walk back and forth on the rickety bridge repeatedly to get the perfect shot was incredible. Thank you for letting me use you and being my "Molly."

Lezli King, the hiking guru, who sacrificed some of our precious dinner date time to read the chapters and offer input, and sent emails of advice, input, and answers to my questions. Thank you!

Jordan Armistead, the one and only real estate agent I considered to help formulate the plotline surrounding Molly's career. You were incredible!!

Julie Harrell, my sweet friend who spent an ungodly amount of hours reading drafts and listening to me go on and on about the book. Our lives are parallel as far as the empty nest is concerned, so your input and suggestions were always welcome and amazing.

Kara Trella, my beautiful cousin who took time out of her life to provide input, feedback, and editing. I have never been more nervous than I was when I hit send on the email. She is without a doubt the best writer I've ever known, but her constructive criticism, story feedback, and high praise were things I'll cherish forever. After a year of terrible loss and pain, I've learned some of the best lessons from you.

CPSIA information can be obtained
at www.ICGtesting.com
Printed in the USA
LVHW050242280122
709355LV00015B/1745